G000054677

Timber Circles
in the East

Patrick Taylor

POLYSTAR PRESS

ISBN 978 1 907154 60 7

Timber Circles in the East

Published by Polystar Press

277 Cavendish Street	62 Angel Street
Ipswich	Hadleigh
Suffolk	Suffolk
IP3 8BQ	IP7 5EY
(01473) 434604	(01473) 824896
polystar@ntlworld.com	polystar@btinternet.com

ISBN 978 1 907154 60 7

All rights reserved.
This book is protected by copyright.
No part of it may be reproduced, stored in a
retrieval system, or transmitted, in any form
or by any means, electronic, mechanical,
photocopying, recording or otherwise, without
the written permission of the author or publisher.

Every attempt has been made to trace accurate
ownership of copyrighted material in this book.
Errors and omissions will be corrected in
subsequent editions, provided that
notification is sent to the publisher.

© Patrick Taylor 2015

Typeset by nattygrafix

Printed by
R Booth Ltd, The Praze, Penryn

CONTENTS

For Jake Bray

'Best Boy'

"For in and out, above, about, below,
'Tis nothing but a magic Shadow-show,
Play'd in a Box whose Candle is the Sun,
Round which we Phantom Figures come and go."

Rubaiyat of Omar Khayyam,
the Astronomer Poet of Persia,
Done into English by Edward FitzGerald

INTRODUCTION

painting: rosie perkins

Although the author was put down as 'amateur astronomer' by Ruggles, he considers himself neither of these, rather a professional in his own fields of Architecture and Building Conservation, with the added bonus of a first class honours degree in Mathematics, and a keen interest in our past.

The studies in this book have already been published in part, but pulling them all together into a single volume is something that someone, someday would have had to do. Forty years ago, at the time Alexander Thom's works on the stone circles were being vigorously discussed, the concept of 'timber circle' barely existed, except to describe a few examples of post-holes occasionally found in association with stone circles and then thought to have been early trial versions of a less permanent nature. Recent discoveries have boosted the numbers considerably and shown timber circles to be far more widespread than was formerly thought. We have enough here in the east of England to demonstrate that the variety of forms and sizes seen amongst the stone circles is repeated here in timber, as shown by the frontispiece to each section where they are all illustrated at a scale of 1:200.

The new way to describe them should apparently be 'timber rings', following on from the idea of 'stone rings', which does at least acknowledge the oft found plans that are flattened or egg-shaped, but we will stick with timber circles here, to be quite sure people know what we are referring to. On the ground the fact that a circle's plan is flattened or otherwise distorted is not usually apparent without detailed measurement.

1

Stone circles fall into a fairly well defined category of archaeological remains, commonly found across the western two thirds of the British Isles. Indeed they seem not to stray further east than about 1° west, the eastern counties of England being totally without such megalithic remains.

A more recent, and not dissimilar, distribution can be found amongst the country's vernacular buildings, with stone extensively used where it is readily available in the west, but scarce in the east where a fine tradition of timber-framed buildings now prevails.

photo: polystar

medieval carving, angel house, glemsford

Recent discoveries of what have become known as 'timber circles', both in the east and the west, lead to a scenario where it seems the same culture pervaded the land as a whole, but was expressed in the east only in the form of timber monuments. These if built in timber and maintained, like our more recent vernacular houses, would have proved nearly as long lasting in the short term, certainly usable for a generation or two. It is only in the longer perspective of the archaeological record that we get stone circles along with stone tombs and standing stones in the west surviving for millennia, whilst those constructions of timber have ultimately decayed.

The timbers did not last except in the ground, where archaeologists now find if they are lucky 'pipe holes', signalled by the darker earth of rotted wood within holes dug into the natural local substrate. Timber circles may seem more scarce, simply because they leave no visible traces above ground, but the truth may simply be that we have not yet found them all.

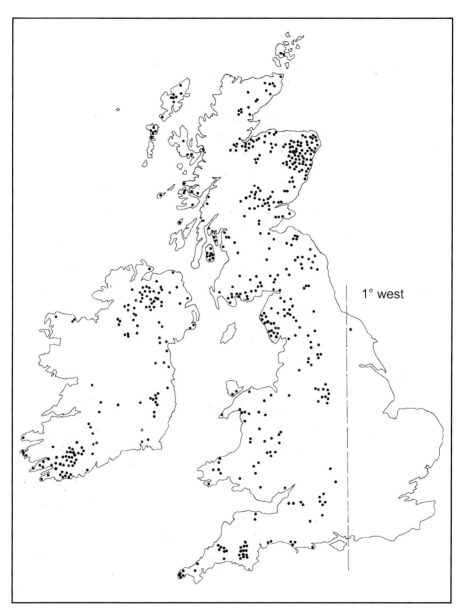

Map of Stone Circle Sites (after Burl)

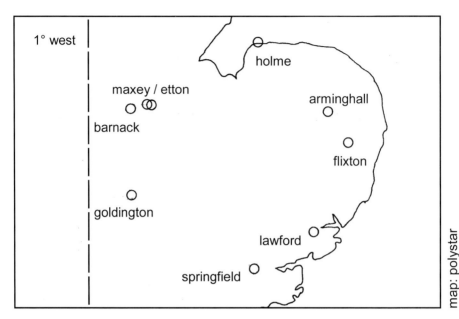

1° west

maxey / etton

barnack

holme

arminghall

flixton

goldington

lawford

springfield

map: polystar

Whilst many a western stone circle site has now been found to have had a timber precursor, it seems the eastern sites were only ever timber and the record remains scant as they are not often found. Neolithic man certainly had the capability of moving stone over long distances, as witnessed by the famous bluestones at Stonehenge, sourced from the Preseli Hills of west Wales, but in the east he seems to have been content to stick with the more readily available local timber.

The distribution of the timber circles might be seen to be a circle in itself superimposed on the map of eastern England, however it should be remembered that these are usually river valley sites and their distribution is very much a result of the East Anglian watershed.

The purpose of the stone circles has been a source of much speculation over the years, not least because most have little else to offer in terms of archaeological remains than the stones themselves. Very little has ever been found in the way of domestic or funerary material to pin such a use on them and the same seems to apply to the timber circles as well. 'Ceremonial' or 'Ritual' is the general consensus, particularly as many such circles can be found in relatively close proximity to both domestic and funerary sites of similar age. We seem to have little left to read these monuments by, other than the actual monuments themselves, but their ground plans and positions within the larger landscape give us something further to observe, record and speculate about.

picture: william cotton (1827)

Boscawen-Ûn Circle in Sancred

Stone circles generally survive an archaeological dig, but the timber circles once dug only survive on paper as plans and published reports. It is this paper record that the author has had to rely on for most of his information and the difference in its quality is very telling over the years of how these monuments have been regarded.

The older material will be seen to have less well defined north points on the plans, even magnetic north sometimes being used, and scales that are unclear and difficult to read. One particular site was dug in two halves with a ten year gap between the digs and then published with two half plans, not really appreciating the presence of the circle of post-holes, which they considered to simply be a fence. More recent material is usually more thorough with every feature numbered, described in intimate detail and gridded up relative to the national grid, which can be easily related to true north, very useful when considering the astronomy visible from a site.

This subject thus mainly has a 'paper heritage' which will in all likelihood soon be a digital one. Many of the illustrations used in this volume have had to be copied from various archaeological reports and papers, simply because that is all we have left that can tell us anything. Permission has certainly been sought for all copied material, and has fortunately been granted for most in time for publication. The images concerned are after all part of our heritage and we should have as much right to reproduce them as we would our own photograph of a visited stone monument.

Dance Maine at Bolleit, in the Parish of Burian.

picture: william cotton (1827)

In the 1960's and 1970's Professor Alexander Thom, a Scottish engineer, published the results of his decades of work accurately surveying stone circles, mainly within Scotland. His theories greatly upset the archaeological profession, not least because he brought a degree of scientific investigation into what up to then had largely been a field dominated by the Humanities. Basically the archaeologists did not understand his scientific methods, which included various elements of geometry, astronomy and statistical analysis, supporting a theory which proposed that Neolithic man was brighter than he had hitherto been given credit for.

It must be remembered that at this time archaeology was already in turmoil trying to assimilate the revolution that was radiocarbon dating. Because of the earlier dating involved, this seemed to imply that every development in the west was not now the result of the gentle diffusion of ideas from the east, where all civilisation had been thought to originate. Thom's ideas were equally challenging, proposing that Neolithic man had laid out his circles with a standard unit of length dubbed the Megalithic Yard, using geometry supposedly discovered by the Greeks a millennium later, and sited to take advantage of distant landscape pointers allowing accurate observation of the motions of the sun and moon.

Part of the problem seems to have been the erroneous idea that Thom's results implied that Neolithic man had equal access to a theodolite, or an understanding of our modern theories of geometry and celestial motion.

photo: polystar

This was not the case and what we need to remember here is that Neolithic man on these islands is certainly amongst our own ancestors and only some 200 generations back. He may not have had our questionably superior technology, but he was essentially the same as us genetically and amongst his number there would undoubtedly have been the occasional Newton or Einstein capable of studying, recording and interpreting the motions of the sun and moon.

Obviously there was a different worldview to our own, but that does not mean that it was wrong; their observations of the heavenly bodies were essentially made relative to fixed points on a distant horizon and their results within that field of view would have been as repeatable there as any of our own scientific experiments are in the laboratory today.

Similarly their geometry may not have had the certainty of an overriding theory like that of Pythagoras, whereby the sum of the squares of the two smaller sides of any right angled triangle is equal to the square of the hypotenuse, whatever values those sides took. However the use of whole number Pythagorean triples to set out right angles would have been an easy skill to assimilate and pass on using simple numbers.

Before we get to examine the timber circles themselves, the next two sections will take a closer look at what Neolithic astronomy and geometry might have been like.

REFERENCES

Burl, A. 1976 *The Stone Circles of the British Isles* Yale UP

Gibson, A. 1998 *Stonehenge & Timber Circles* Tempus

Harding, J. 2003 *Henge Monuments of the British Isles* Tempus

Heath, R. 2007 *Alexander Thom: Cracking the Stone Age Code*
Bluestone Press

Loveday, R.   2006   *Inscribed Across the Landscape: The Cursus Enigma*
Tempus

North, J. 1996 *Stonehenge: Neolithic Man and the Cosmos* HarperCollins

Parker Pearson, M. 2012 *Stonehenge* Simon & Schuster

Pitts, M. 2000 *Hengeworld* Arrow

Ruggles, C.L.N. (ed) 1988 *Records in Stone Papers in Memory of
Alexander Thom* Cambridge UP

Ruggles, C. 1999 *Astronomy in Prehistoric Britain and Ireland* Yale UP

Thom, A. 1967 *Megalithic Sites in Britain* Oxford UP

Thom, A. 1971 *Megalithic Lunar Observatories* Oxford UP

Thom, A. & A.S. 1978 *Megalithic Remains in Britain and Brittany* Oxford UP

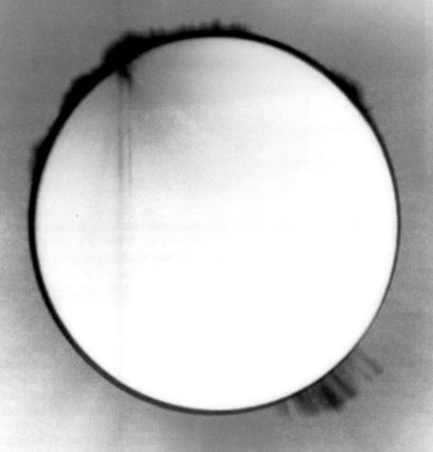

photo: nasa - apollo 8 (1968)

Whilst the modern scientific paradigm has indeed conquered the complexities of the motions of the heavenly bodies, to the extent of confirming a century ago the eccentricities of Mercury's motions using relativity theory, these motions remain beyond the understanding of the man in the street other than at a very general level. Most people can grasp the basic heliocentric view with a rotating earth, orbiting the sun, with the moon orbiting in its turn about the earth, giving rise to our daily, annual and monthly cycles respectively.

Despite this there are common misunderstandings such as the 'dark side of the moon', a place which does not exist as any one side of the moon is indeed dark at a particular time, the other side being fully lit by the sun. However over just less than a month the moon experiences its own 'day', any location being lit by the sun for about two weeks, then dark for two more.

The term 'far side of the moon' is far more accurate as the moon in its orbit actually rotates just once each cycle, keeping roughly the same near side facing the earth and the same far side out of our gaze forever. 'Earth rise on the moon' as photographed by one of the Apollo missions is thus also a misnomer as from a lunar perspective, whilst the sun would come up and traverse the sky over two weeks before setting, at most locations the earth is either visible or not, more or less constantly visible in one position in the moon's sky, or if one was on the far side, never visible at all.

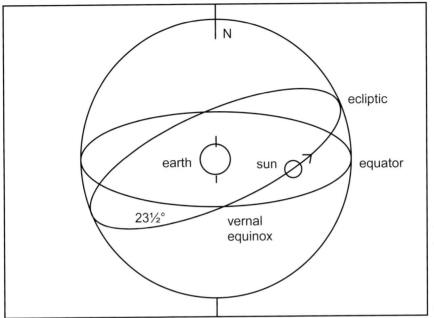

diagram: polystar

Here on earth with our modern framework of knowledge, we can imagine the sun's motions in terms of a celestial sphere that shares our poles and equator, a kind of layer beyond the surface of the earth within which the heavenly bodies move. The sun and 'fixed' stars can be imagined to rotate around us on this daily, whilst over the course of a year the unfixed sun travels around the celestial sphere on a great circle set at about 23½° to the equatorial plane. It is thus high in northern skies during our summer and low in winter, its maximum and minimum declinations (angles from the equatorial plane) being +23½° and −23½° respectively.

At zero and increasing declination, as the sun crosses the equator it rises in the east and sets in the west so that we have twelve hours of day followed by twelve hours of night, a time known as the vernal equinox and mirrored by the similar autumnal equinox six months later when the declination is again zero, but decreasing towards the darker days of winter. Relative to the fixed stars of the celestial sphere, the vernal equinox is currently at the first point of Aries, but because the equinoxes precess, even this point is not fixed and cycles around the equatorial plane of the sphere over some 26,000 years, amazingly something the ancient Mayans may have been aware of.

Without the concept of a celestial sphere, Neolithic man did not have the luxury of our heliocentric overview, and would not even have even dreamt of a lunacentric point of view. He observed things from a purely geocentric position, with his feet firmly on the ground.

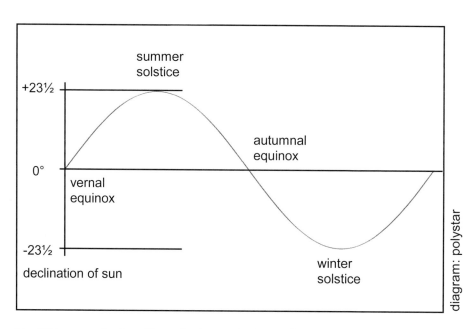

diagram: polystar

Neolithic man had neither clock, sextant nor theodolite to assist with his observations, his only gauge for measuring the motions of the heavenly bodies being the fixed horizon against which they rose in the east and set in the west. In terms of size and presence, the sun and moon with their associated yearly and monthly cycles, would surely have been at the forefront of his interest. It is only sheer coincidence that from earth they both present to an observer a disc of about half a degree width and Neolithic man would have been oblivious to the fact that one of these bodies is both considerably larger and further away by a factor of about 400 times.

It is almost certain that the sun, being the simpler in its apparent motions, would have been the first to yield up its mysteries. As we understand it the earth's equatorial plane is tilted at an angle of 23½° to the plane of the ecliptic within which the earth orbits around the sun. Thus at one time of year, say northern summer, the north pole is tilted towards the sun, presenting us with longer days, more opportunity to absorb radiation and consequently warmer summer weather. Six months later with the north pole pointing away from the sun (and itself in darkness) we get the shorter, colder days of northern winter.

To Neolithic man, the annual cycle of the sun's motion would have been detectable on the horizon. The sun rises and sets nearer north in the summer and nearer south in the winter, either side of the average east-west transit seen at the equinoxes in spring and autumn.

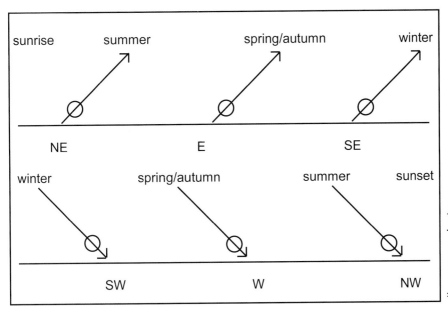

sunrise	summer	spring/autumn	winter

NE   E   SE

winter	spring/autumn	summer	sunset

SW   W   NW

diagram: polystar

Within the latitudes of the British Isles the variation away from east-west is more pronounced in the north than in the south. The extremes of this are further north, where during arctic summers and winters the sun either stays up all day or is permanently below the horizon, or further south around the equator where the transit is basically always east-west, regardless of season.

The greater variations available in the north of Britain would have enabled greater accuracy there, engendering the likelihood that any advances in observational techniques would originate in the north. Recent archaeological investigations at Ness of Brodgar, between the Stones of Stenness and the Ring of Brodgar, on Orkney seem to be suggesting an early northern origin to the megalithic culture that appears to come to full fruition much later at Stonehenge far to the south.

Whatever the origins, the basic motion of the sun through the year could easily be tracked by observing its rising and setting points on the horizon. When this is roughly east-west at the equinoxes in spring and autumn, the positions of rise and set are changing daily at their fastest. At the extremes however, we have the solstices (literally sun standing still) where the positions hardly change day to day, reaching maximum positions that would form natural pointers to constant and repeatable times of year, the reliable basis for a calendar.

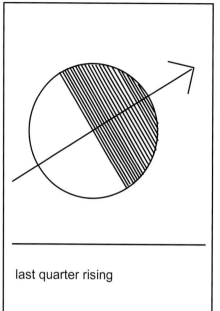

last quarter rising

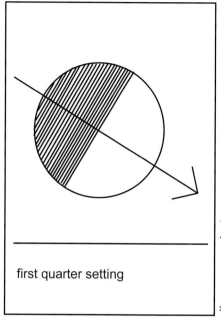

first quarter setting

diagrams: polystar

Stonehenge itself is well known for its midsummer sunrise orientation, but also has built in indicators towards the maximum positions on the horizon reached by the moon. We will see later that as minor a monument as the 'Seahenge' timber circle at Holme has been positioned to take advantage of a natural landscape pointer towards the midwinter sunset.

The sun's apparent motions as seen from the earth are relatively simple and straightforward compared to those of the moon. Undoubtedly Neolithic man would have wanted to follow on from his understanding of the sun to investigate the motions of the moon, a challenge if ever there was one.

Whilst the sun can be observed (weather permitting) rising and setting every day with a single annual cycle to its movements, the moon can only reliably be seen both rising and setting at the time of full moon, with periods before and after that when its respective setting or rising only can be observed. Around first quarter, the moon is not very visible when it rises as the sun will already be out, so that only the setting can be reliably observed during the evening after sunset. Similarly around last quarter it will not be very visible when it sets as the sun will still be up, so that only the rise is properly observable early in the morning before sunrise.

On top of these observational difficulties, essentially requiring long watches through the night, the motions of the moon are manifold and complex.

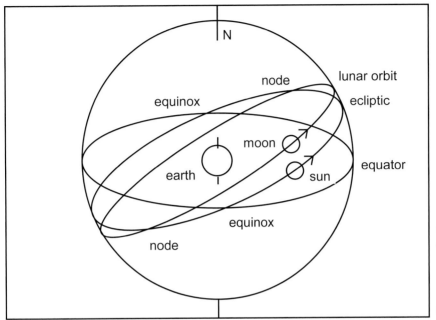

diagram: polystar

The plane in which the moon orbits the earth is not quite that of the ecliptic, being inclined at an angle of 5.15° to that plane within which the sun appears to move. If it were not so inclined we would have two eclipses every month, a lunar one at full moon and a solar one two weeks later at new moon, together with a good deal less mystery.

The two planes of orbit of the sun and moon intersect at 'nodes' and an eclipse will only occur if both bodies are at a node at the same time: a lunar eclipse if they are opposing nodes, a solar eclipse if they coincide. Most of the time the positions of both sun and moon are away from the nodes and they pass each other without being noticed here on earth.

Around midsummer the sun will be at its highest positive declination and a new moon will pass somewhere within 5.15° of this, but being only 0.5° wide itself, it is unlikely to cross the sun's path as seen from earth. Two weeks later the full moon will be low in the sky with a large negative declination and is also unlikely to intercept the earth's nearby shadow.

Around midwinter the opposite holds with the sun and new moon at their lowest, with large negative declinations, and the full moon high in the sky with a large positive declination. Thus each month as the moon orbits the earth it will be seen at a wide range of declinations, but these do have their limits. The widest range occurs when the nodes coincide with the equinoctial points where the ecliptic meets the equator.

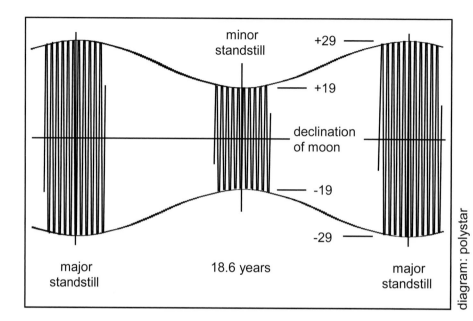

diagram: polystar

At the major standstill: the 5.15° is additive and the moon's declination will vary widely between about ± 29°, whilst at the minor standstill it is subtractive and the moon's declination will only range between about ± 19°.

I say 'about' here because although the angle between the sun's and moon's orbits remains fairly constant, the sun's declination has varied over time, having been 23.93° around 2000 BC and about 23.44° now, and there is a further variation in the moon's orbit we have yet to examine. The full cycle from major standstill to minor and back again takes some 18.6 years, so major and minor standstills are about 9.3 years apart. Effectively what is happening here is that the nodes between the two planes of orbit precess relative to the celestial sphere with a period of 18.6 years.

Using the horizon as a gauge, it would take some years of observation to pin this second cycle down, but again being in the north of Britain would have been to an observer's advantage. A winter's full moon at major standstill would be very high in the sky, rising and setting well north of the midsummer sun, whilst a similar summer's full moon would be very low and maximum use could be made of distant landscape features to calibrate any variations. The difference between these two situations six months apart is useful in conceptualising that, counter-intuitively, when looking at a diagram of the moon's declination month by month, the full and new moons generally occur away from the limiting maximum or minimum declinations.

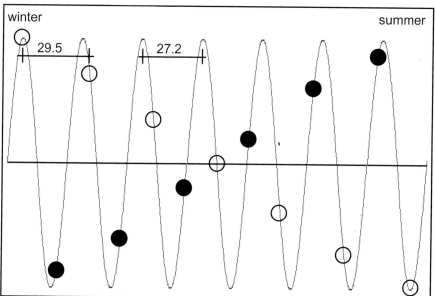

diagram: polystar

This is perhaps obvious if one considers a winter's full moon at maximum +29° declination, which will always fail to capture the earth's shadow as cast by the sun at minimum -23½° declination. Month by month the ensuing full moons will occur at lower declinations, and be more likely to line up opposite the sun, until six months later it will be around the minimum -29° and once again miss the earth's shadow cast by a sun at maximum +23½°. In general eclipses around a standstill occur near an equinox, whilst those between standstills occur near a solstice. The slippage here is caused by the difference between the 'draconic' month (27.2 days) of the moon's actual orbit and the longer 'synodic' month (29.5 days) of its visible cycle, full moon to full moon. The monthly maximum and minimum declinations of the moon thus usually occur at times other than full or new moon, which are times when observation is the more difficult and limited, as we noted earlier.

Another difficulty here is the speed of the moon's progress, doing in two weeks what the sun does in six months. Whilst the solstice can be observed in a leisurely way over several days with little variation, the extreme position of the moon would more often than not occur inbetween two of our limited observation periods which are of necessity at best a day apart. Pinning this down would be like trying to observe the solstice with twelve days between observations: possible but difficult and requiring a degree of interpolation. Nevertheless with a long enough period of observation, using only the rising and setting points on the horizon, a pattern for the moon's motions would eventually emerge.

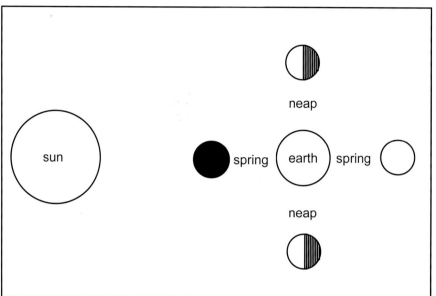

diagram: polystar

The interesting part is that on top of these two cycles of lunar motion, there is a third cycle going on, a lunar wobble or minor perturbation of around 0.15°, about a third of the width of the moon's disc, which if observed would have allowed Neolithic man to predict eclipses.

We know that the moon at its quarter phases leads to the less extreme 'neap' tides here on earth because the gravitational pull on the sea from it is perpendicular to that of the sun, not in line as at full or new moon, when we get higher 'spring' tides. The reverse of this is that the moon at its quarter position is held less strongly and is more free to develop any wobble in its orbit as the sun's and earth's gravitational pulls are acting at right angles to each other, again not in line as at full or new moon.

The orbit of the moon has indeed developed such a wobble, a third cycle on top of the monthly and 18.6 year cycles. It amounts to only some 9 minutes of arc, ± 0.15°, enough to be detected on a body itself only 0.5° across, and has a time period of 346.6 days. This is twice the time taken for the sun to go from one node to the next, and is known as an 'eclipse year'.

The important thing here is that when this wobble is at its maximum, and altering the moon's declination at major standstill, the moon will be at a quarter position and the new and full moons either side of it will thus be near the nodes. Now because these are new or full moons, the sun also has to be near a node and we have ideal conditions for an eclipse to occur.

Latitude = 50°			
		Subtract for	Add for
°Ampl	°Decl	+1°Latitude	+1°Altitude
0	0.00	0.00	0.77
5	3.21	0.07	0.77
10	6.41	0.14	0.77
15	9.58	0.20	0.78
20	12.70	0.27	0.78
25	15.76	0.34	0.79
30	18.75	0.41	0.81
35	21.63	0.48	0.82
40	24.40	0.55	0.84
45	27.03	0.61	0.86
50	29.50	0.68	0.88
55	31.77	0.74	0.90
60	33.83	0.80	0.92
65	35.63	0.86	0.94
70	37.16	0.91	0.96
75	38.38	0.95	0.98
80	39.27	0.98	0.99
85	39.82	0.99	1.00
90	40.00	1.00	1.00

Part of Professor Thom's Table 3.1 (1967) for the lower latitudes in the British Isles is shown adjoining. It allows an amplitude measured from due east or west on the horizon or from a map to be converted into a measure of declination as used in modern astronomy.

Simple linear interpolation is used to read the second column from the first, and the third and fourth columns allow adjustments to be included for latitude of the site and altitude of the horizon respectively. (If negative amplitude, then negative declination, then add for latitude and always add for altitude.)

Eclipses occur all over the world, not all visible from any one point and they only last a limited time, but it seems that Neolithic man's observations had detected the minor perturbation in the moon's motion and correlated it to the increased likelihood of eclipses at roughly the same times. The fact that the very first timber circle examined by the author (at Flixton) is accurately aligned to maximum northwards moonset accords with this idea that Neolithic man was interested in this phenomenon. Not only interested, but in a world where agriculture was taking root, intimate knowledge of the motions of the sun and moon would have been powerful knowledge.

Bound up in all this there is the notion of a calendar whereby crop sowing and gathering could be made more efficient along with the knowledge of the tides allowing the transport of goods by water to be best undertaken. The sun and moon were probably the basis of any 'religion' or system of beliefs held by Neolithic man and the ability to predict the rare and mysterious occurrence of an eclipse, the conjunction of these two bodies, something to be wondered at by those not in the know.

Without a written record it is difficult to know what was believed, but the record left us in stone and timber certainly shows that considerable effort went into the construction of these monuments, which would not have been done without good cause. Furthermore with the addition of timber circles into the archaeological picture, it seems this quest for knowledge was indeed undertaken across the entire British land mass.

REFERENCES

Heath, R. 2007 *Alexander Thom: Cracking the Stone Age Code*
Bluestone Press

North, J. 1996 *Stonehenge: Neolithic Man and the Cosmos* HarperCollins

Ruggles, C.L.N. (ed) 1988 *Records in Stone Papers in Memory of Alexander Thom* Cambridge UP

Ruggles, C. 1999 *Astronomy in Prehistoric Britain and Ireland* Yale UP

Thom, A. 1967 *Megalithic Sites in Britain* Oxford UP

Thom, A. 1971 *Megalithic Lunar Observatories* Oxford UP

Thom, A. & A.S. 1978 *Megalithic Remains in Britain and Brittany* Oxford UP

Assuming Neolithic man took an interest in the motions of the heavenly bodies, in particular the sun and moon, we have seen that the former would be fairly yielding of its secrets, whilst the latter might remain mysterious for some time, requiring many years of observation to find its pattern.

In order to pin down the finer details of the moon's motions, a site for observation could have been carefully chosen so that the limiting declinations at rising and setting would be observed against some notable distant landscape feature, a topographical foresight.

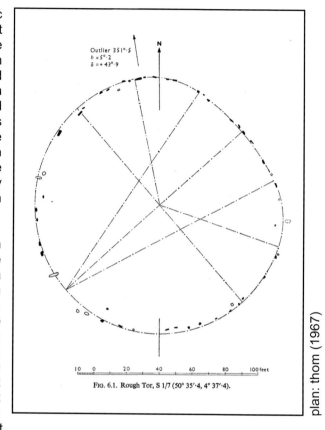

Outlier 351°·5
h = 5°·2
δ = + 43°·9

Fig. 6.1. Rough Tor, S 1/7 (50° 35'·4, 4° 37'·4).

plan: thom (1967)

Failing this one would have to erect one's own foresights for the purpose, which may well be the case in the west, where many a single standing stone can be found slightly distant from a stone circle. Of course the timber circles may well have had their own lone timber counterparts to these, set apart from the circle, but finding such long decayed remains in the form of buried post-holes would be relatively difficult; the timber circles are scarce enough themselves and usually only come to light when something more substantial such as a later ring ditch on the same site is being dug.

Far better and more accurate is to take some distant landscape feature as the pointer: a hilltop or a valley providing a bump or notch respectively on the horizon against which things can be gauged. All that would then be needed would be some local feature within the monument to direct one's attention in roughly the right direction.

photo: polystar

One way part of a circular monument can be made to stand out and provide a direction in which to look, is by altering the heights of the posts, but this is difficult to establish in timber circles, when usually all we have are just the post holes to tell us anything. General rules about the height of posts relative to the diameters or depths of their holes can provide some clues, but this is not totally reliable.

At Seahenge the orientation towards midwinter sunset over the cliffs, where Hunstanton has subsequently been built, seems to have been provided by posts either side of the 'circle' remaining as complete rounds of timber with bark on all sides, as compared to the remaining posts which are generally halved trees with the bark set on the outer face of the monument.

The plan shape of this particular monument shows another way in which a direction can be implied, namely by introducing an asymmetry whereby the plan only reflects along a single axis as opposed to every axis as in a true circle. It is not clear exactly where the symmetrical axis implied at Seahenge is pointing, other than at a nearby hilltop, whereas at Stonehenge the horseshoe shaped setting of trilithons magnificently delineates the axis of the monument towards midsummer sunrise. There is something similar in timber at the Arminghall site south of Norwich, the open horseshoe there pointing towards midwinter sunset over Chapel Hill, a notable local landscape feature.

FLATTENED CIRCLES

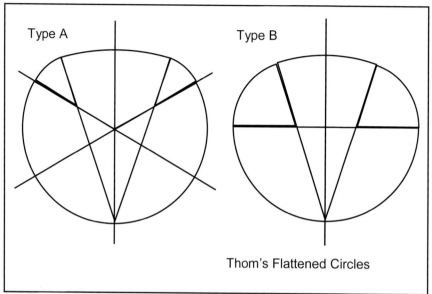

Type A

Type B

Thom's Flattened Circles

plans: polystar

Another way to introduce an axis of symmetry seems to have been the flattened circle, many stone circle examples being cited by Thom and mostly attributable to two slightly differing basic plans.

Thom's type A flattened circle consists of two thirds of a true circle, with 240° of arc, easily set out as four abutting equilateral triangles using the same measure. The two radii containing this are then halved and short arcs of half the original radius continue the curve to form two 'shoulders' between which the shape is completed by a longer arc drawn from a centre midway around the original circular arc.

Thom found many stone circle examples employing this shape in Scotland, and our eastern example is the timber circle at Lawford, missed as such by the archaeologists because they dug the site in two halves about ten years apart and did not seem to have had the sense to plot their two sites onto a single plan for publication.

When trying to establish an axis for such a monument, much complicated statistical analysis can be done trying to find lines of best fit to various geometrical shapes from lines to circles and various combinations of arcs. In my experience however, the simple exercise of reflected overlay is the best, as it uses the human eye and brain to do the computing by intuition.

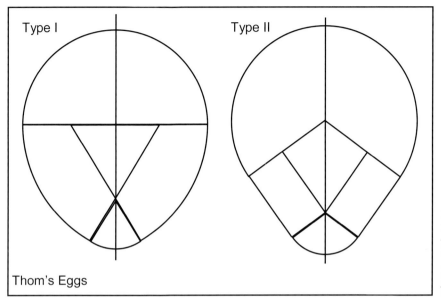

Type I

Type II

Thom's Eggs

plans: polystar

Thom's type B flattened circle is somewhat similar to type A, but only uses a semicircle of 180° of arc as its basis. The diameter thus formed is divided into three to find centres for the two smaller arcs forming shoulders, this time with radius two thirds that of the original circle. The flattened portion joining these is again formed as an arc centred halfway around the original semi-circular arc.

Both these constructions have an unusual property in that the circumference in each is very nearly three times the diameter of the basic circle, the longest diameter of the shape. If as is believed, Neolithic man was interested in mensuration, such a construction would have been far more satisfactory than a true circle with its ratio of circumference to diameter of π (3.14159...), a number that particularly perturbed the ancient Greeks with its irrationality. The type A circle has π' equal to 3.059, whilst for type B π' is 2.957.

Thom also found a variant on type A, which he called type D, in which the radii are subdivided 2:1 so that the shoulders have a radius two thirds that of the main 240° circle. This has a worse value for π' of 3.084 and seems to have been the setting out adopted for the circle at Rough Tor on Bodmin Moor in Cornwall, shown on pages 22 and 23. The axis of this stone circle runs sharply uphill to the north-east and when the high altitude of the horizon is taken into consideration the axis most likely demarcates the northernmost rising of the moon.

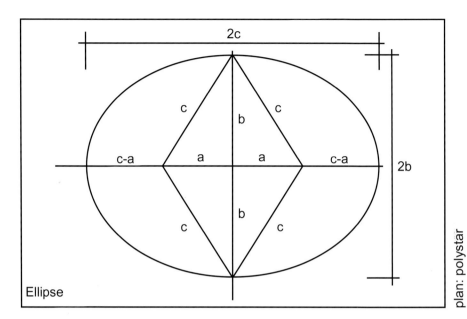

Ellipse

plan: polystar

Interestingly, and perhaps worryingly for these deliberations, there is a modification to the type B flattened circle with a shoulder radius three quarters that of the main semicircle, which would have given π' as 3.001, but this appears not to have been used! Moving swiftly on, Thom also found various egg-shaped plans in the Scottish stone circles, his types I and II layouts based on paired back to back Pythagorean (3,4,5) triangles, the vertices of which give the centres for various arcs forming the eggs.

Pythagorean triples are also useful in constructing ellipses, particularly if one wants the major and minor axes to be multiples of a set measure. A typical Pythagorean triple (a,b,c) where $a^2 + b^2 = c^2$ will yield an ellipse with minor axis 2b and major axis 2c and can be constructed using a rope 2c long, fixed to focal points 2a apart. The special ellipse with ratio of perimeter to longest diameter $\pi' = 3.000$ will have a minor:major ratio, b/c = 0.9088.

None of the smaller Pythagorean triples produce ellipses anywhere near this ideal, the best perhaps being (5,12,13) where b/c = 0.9231 and $\pi' = 3.022$. But then according to Thom, of fifteen 'definite ellipses' he surveyed, only one is based on a true Pythagorean triple, the (12,35,37) at Daviot near Inverness in Scotland. Although he seems to have used these triangles extensively, it is unlikely that Neolithic man saw them as examples of Pythagoras' Theorem whereby the square of the hypotenuse equals the sum of the squares of the two shorter sides.

	1	2	3	4	5 m
1	(0,2,2)	(3,4,5)	(8,6,10)	(15,8,17)	(24,10,26)
2	(-3,4,5)	(0,8,8)	(5,12,13)	(12,16,20)	(21,20,29)
3	(-8,6,10)	(-5,12,13)	(0,18,18)	(7,24,25)	(16,30,34)
4	(-15,8,17)	(-12,16,20)	(-7,24,25)	(0,32,32)	(9,40,41)
5	(-24,10,26)	(-21,20,29)	(-16,30,34)	(-9,40,41)	(0,50,50)
n					

table: polystar

However the fact that these numbers made right angles would have been known, and it is likely that Neolithic man also used quasi-Pythagorean triples where the sums are a touch out. Examples of triples where $a^2 + b^2 = c^2 + 1$ are easily found, in fact there are two for every true Pythagorean triple. Two of the ellipses in Thom's definite list use such numbers: Lee Moor in Devon uses the triangle (16,23,28), which can be derived from (15,20,25), whilst Ballinluig in Perthshire uses (22,31,38) derivable from (21,28,35).

A smaller triple with this quasi-Pythagorean property is (7,11,13), derived from (6,8,10) and believed to have been the basis of the setting out of the Flixton timber circle in north Suffolk. Even this relatively small triangle has an error less than $\frac{1}{2}°$ in the right angle, and any such triangle with a larger hypotenuse would render the error (given by $\sin^{-1}(1/2ab)$) virtually undetectable. A table showing the possible smaller quasi-Pythagorean triples along with a few where $a^2 + b^2 = c^2 - 1$ is given overleaf.

To understand the derivation of these quasi-Pythagorean triples, we first need to understand the Pythagorean ones. These are covered by Euclid's formula whereby triples (a,b,c) for which $a^2 + b^2 = c^2$ are all either of the form $a = m^2 - n^2$, $b = 2mn$ and $c = m^2 + n^2$, or are multiples of such. A simple piece of algebra will confirm this and it can be seen that (3,4,5) arises in the simple case of m = 2 and n = 1. The table above shows what we get for the smaller values of m and n.

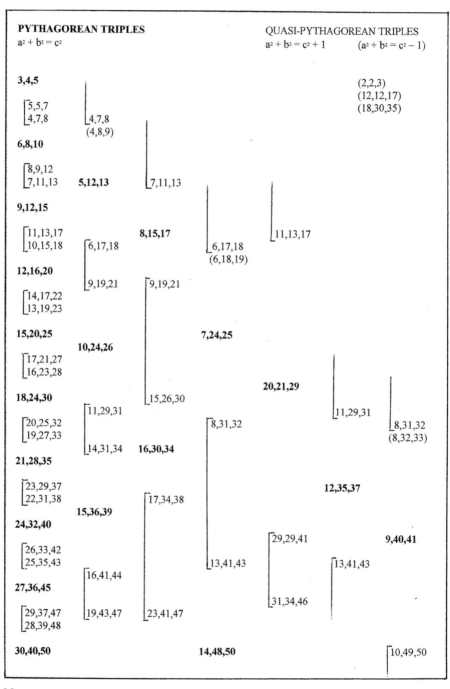

	1	2	3	4	5 k
1	(3,4,5)	(8,6,10)	(15,8,17)	(24,10,26)	(35,12,37)
2	(5,12,13)	(12,16,20)	(21,20,29)	(32,24,40)	(45,28,53)
3	(7,24,25)	(16,30,34)	(27,36,45)	(40,42,58)	(55,48,73)
4	(9,40,41)	(20,48,52)	(33,56,65)	(48,64,80)	(65,72,97)
5	(11,60,61)	(24,70,74)	(38,80,89)	(56,90,106)	(75,100,125)
n					

table: polystar

The triples in the bottom left of the table duplicate those in the top right with a negative number included because m < n, whilst those on the main diagonal, where m = n, all include a zero and two sides the same and are of the general form $(0,2m^2,2m^2)$, the positive values those of the numbers of electrons in successive shells of an atom.

The first diagonal above, where m = n + 1, produces classic Pythagorean triples of the form (a,b,b+1). The next diagonal up has m = n + 2 and triples of the form (a,b,b+4) and the one after that with m = n + 3 produces triples of the form (a,b,b+9). The general case is thus the kth diagonal above the main one with m = n + k and triples of the form $(a,b,b+k^2)$.

If we tabulate k against n, as above, we lose the negative versions and can see these various series of Pythagorean triples, now arranged in columns. Now it can be shown by some slightly more complicated algebra than we avoided two pages ago, that for each triple (a,b,c) for which $a^2 + b^2 = c^2$, there are two further ones (d,e,f) for which $d^2 + e^2 = f^2 + 1$, related by the formulae d = a ± 1, e = b ± (m+n) / k and f = c ± (m+n) / k. These are the quasi-Pythagorean triples shown in lighter text on the table opposite.

It might be noticed that some of the true Pythagorean triples shown, such as (9,12,15), do not occur in the table above. However in this case if we make m = 2√3, n = √3 and thus k = √3, all the algebra works and we can derive two quasi-Pythagorean triples to accompany it (8,9,12) and (10,15,18).

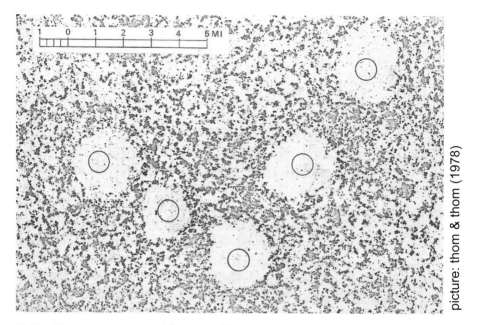

picture: thom & thom (1978)

If Neolithic man was setting out his monuments using these geometric principles, the question naturally arises as to what was his unit of measurement. Thom carried out extensive statistical analysis on his measurements of the diameters of the circles he surveyed and came up with the Megalithic Yard as the basic unit. It was 2.72 feet or 829 millimetres in length and seemed to make sense of his surveys and proposals for how these monuments were set out using the basic geometry we have just examined.

Interestingly a similar statistical analysis of cup and ring marks, incised on many a stone monument and outcrops of bare rock nearby, found a similar unit forty times smaller, dubbed the Megalithic Inch. Additional weight can be given here as some cup and ring marks can be clearly seen to be set out centred on the vertices of (3,4,5) Pythagorean triangles, as shown above.

It should be remembered that the Neolithic period in which this all took place was not peopled by prehistoric men of an earlier species, but by people who share our own genes, only some 200 generations back at its beginning. Although life was short and probably brutal, it is likely that amongst the population there would be the occasional genius of similar stature to Newton or Einstein, whose preoccupation may well have been the motions of the heavenly bodies. Indeed if those bodies were the basis of their beliefs, then the ability to predict the eclipse would bring great power to those that could.

photo: ©ashmolean museum, university of oxford

It would seem that Neolithic man's pre-emption of the Greeks by a millennium or so with his use of Pythagorean triples is not the only example of civilisation not necessarily coming from the east. Numerous carved stone balls dating back to the Neolithic period have been found that appear to demonstrate his knowledge of the Platonic solids.

Around 400 examples of these carved stone balls or 'petrospheres' have been found to date and these are likely to be just the better preserved examples that we can differentiate from otherwise plain rocks. They mostly come from an area of eastern Scotland, now Aberdeenshire, where there is also a prevalence of a special type of stone circle, known as 'recumbent' from the presence on the perimeter of a large laid down monolith.

Most of the balls are about 70mm in diameter although a few occur larger and all seem to have a series of knobs on them exhibiting various geometries. About a tenth of the examples are tetrahedral in their symmetry with 4 knobs, sometimes elaborately carved with spiral patterns. About half the examples have precisely 6 knobs exhibiting well the symmetries of the cube and octahedron, the former if the knobs are flattened and appear like faces (as seen in two of the examples above) but the latter if the knobs protrude and become the vertices of what we see. There are also ten examples with 8 knobs, eight with 12 knobs (which can be seen as dodecahedral if flattened or icosahedral if protruding) and just a couple with 20 knobs.

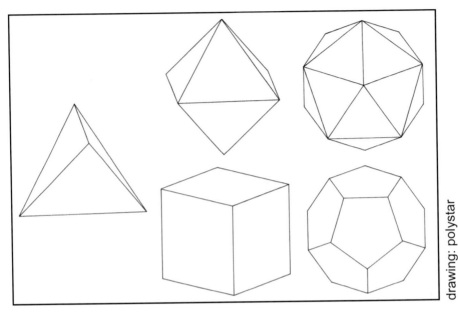

drawing: polystar

Five in number, the Platonic solids are the basic regular three dimensional geometric forms that can be constructed using regular polygons, supposedly first described by Plato. Taking the centres of the faces of any of these as vertex points we can derive another, its dual. They thus comprise two dual pairs, where vertices and faces are interchangeable, and one that is its own dual:

Tetrahedron	{3,3}	4 triangle faces, 4 vertices, 6 edges
Cube	{4,3}	6 square faces, 8 vertices, 12 edges
Octahedron	{3,4}	8 triangle faces, 6 vertices, 12 edges
Dodecahedron	{5,3}	12 pentagon faces, 20 vertices, 30 edges
Icosahedron	{3,5}	20 triangle faces, 12 vertices, 30 edges

The general regular polyhedron is given as {x,y}, indicating that at each vertex there are y x-gons present. The faces thus have symmetry x, the vertices symmetry y and this polyhedron will have a dual given as {y,x}.

We have already seen a lot of the (3,4,5) Pythagorean triple, but here in three dimensions the same three numbers come to light in the symmetries of these regular solids. There are thus only three possible symmetries here and the carved stone balls exhibit them all, but they also include a few other less regular forms.

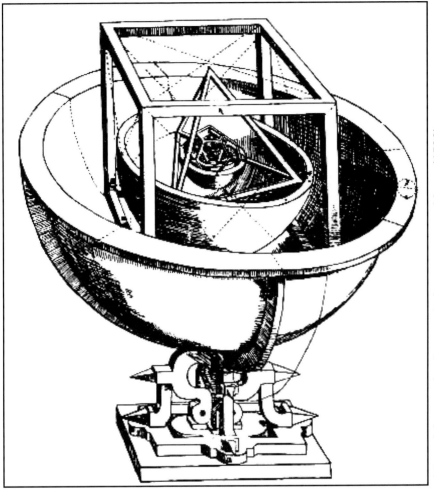

picture: johannes kepler, mysterium cosmographicum (1596)

The Greeks interestingly paired the Platonic solids with the basic elements they thought the world was made of: the tetrahedron went with fire, the cube with earth, the octahedron with air, the icosahedron with water, leaving the dodecahedron to represent the universe as a whole.

Another tantalising link with the cosmos was given by Johannes Kepler in the late 16th Century, when he famously stacked the Platonic solids such that the external sphere of one was the internal sphere of the next, producing a series of concentric spheres like russian dolls, whose radii he thought matched those of the orbits of the inner planets.

It seems that an interest in such universal geometric truths is hard-wired into our species, no less now than five thousand years ago.

REFERENCES

Bradley, R. 1997 *Rock Art and the Prehistory of Atlantic Europe* Routledge

Critchlow, K. 1969 *Order in Space* Thames & Hudson

Critchlow, K. 2007 *Time Stands Still* Floris Books

Heath, R. 2007 *Alexander Thom: Cracking the Stone Age Code*
Bluestone Press

Marshall, D.N. 1977 *Carved Stone Balls* Proc Soc Antiq Scot 108 pp.4-72

Marshall, D.N. 1983 *Further Notes on Carved Stone Balls*
Proc Soc Antiq Scot 113 pp.628-646

Morris, R.W.B. 1977 *Prehistoric Rock Art of Argyll* Dolphin

Morris, R.W.B. 1979 *Prehistoric Rock Art of Galloway and the Isle of Man*
Blandford

Ruggles, C.L.N. (ed) 1988 *Records in Stone Papers in Memory of
Alexander Thom* Cambridge UP

Ruggles, C. 1999 *Astronomy in Prehistoric Britain and Ireland* Yale UP

Taylor, P. 1999 *The Simpler? Polyhedra* Polystar Press

Thom, A. 1967 *Megalithic Sites in Britain* Oxford UP

Thom, A. 1971 *Megalithic Lunar Observatories* Oxford UP

Thom, A. & A.S. 1978 *Megalithic Remains in Britain and Brittany* Oxford UP

INTRODUCTION

photo: stuart boulter ©SCC

This small contribution to the rather obscure field of archaeoastronomy was originally drafted as a paper for consideration by the Suffolk Institute of Archaeology and History in 1997. It was subsequently passed on to Suffolk County Council's Archaeological Service and as a result Clive Ruggles was later asked to look into my claims.

At first sight, in Suffolk Archaeological Service's 1997 annual report, the plan of the then recently excavated 'Neolithic sub-circular enclosure' at Flixton leapt out of the page and said 'stone circle', which being a set of post-holes, it patently was not. Dating to around 2500 BC it was found during the investigation of a later (1700 BC) ring ditch, on a site subsequently excavated for its gravels.

Memories of Alexander Thom's pioneering work on stone circles in the 1970's were reawakened, wherein he claimed to find in them evidence of geometrical setting out using a standard unit of length, the Megalithic Yard (2.72 feet or 829mm). Thom also found impressive astronomical orientations suggesting intimate knowledge of the finer motions of the moon, such as would make eclipse prediction quite feasible. If we can find evidence for such claims in the timber circles now coming to light in the east, it may mean that Thom was right, or alternatively it may mean that we can adapt any plan with clever geometry to show something.

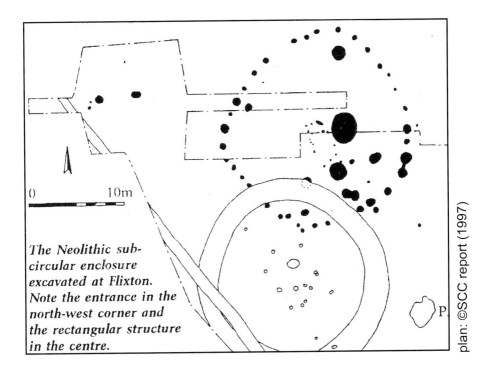

The Neolithic sub-circular enclosure excavated at Flixton. Note the entrance in the north-west corner and the rectangular structure in the centre.

plan: ©SCC report (1997)

0   10m

So what we have here at Flixton (TM 302863) is a set of post-holes, nearly as far east and away from the western tradition of megaliths as we can get. But then of course there was no stone in this area, as is well testified to by the long tradition here of timber-framed building construction, so that what went into these post-holes were presumably large chunks of timber.

At nearly 20 metres in diameter, the circle was certainly not roofed over in a single span, and there seems to be no sign of any regular arrangement of sizeable post-holes within, which might indicate intermediate supports. There also appear to be no indications of any domestic use although some form of small structure, described as sub-rectangular, existed near the centre.

The remains have therefore been classified as a 'sub-circular enclosure', and since phosphate testing did not prove positive, an animal or funerary function has been discounted in favour of a probable ritual function. The similarity in shape to the stone circles has already been noted and in size it comes about midway in the range found for stone circles, so why not just a 'timber circle'?

photo: stuart boulter ©SCC

Perhaps what we see here is the eastern tradition of the same Neolithic people as built the stone circles. Their spread has usually been reckoned in terms of 'western fringe', because that is where their stone monuments survive: Britanny, Cornwall, Wales, Scotland and Ireland. But what if theirs was more of a 'seafaring' tradition and the more perishable evidence has simply been lost in the east?

The Flixton site lies on a flood plain within half a mile of the river Waveney, which in Neolithic times may well have been navigable many more miles upstream; indeed most of Suffolk's Neolithic remains found to date are concentrated on the river valleys.

The notion of a tribal centre based at a circular monument with a distant but visible tomb for the ancestors on nearby higher ground is a model that might fit here. The recent discovery of a long barrow about 400 metres north-east of the circle site bears this idea out. Again not a 'stone monument', but a long oval shaped ditch about 20x45 metres with a series of post holes set internally, those at the north-eastern end seeming to create a façade at the entrance.

The long barrow (TM 305865) predates the circle by about a millennium, but interestingly it has an axis of symmetry pointing to the circle site, so maybe something else was there before the timber circle was built.

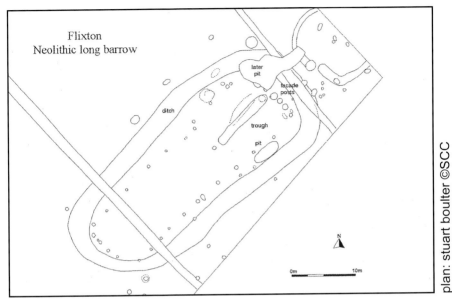

Flixton
Neolithic long barrow

later
pit

facade
posts

ditch

trough

pit

N

0m   10m

plan: stuart boulter ©SCC

Thom proposed that many stone circles of a flattened shape (his type B) were set out using a semi-circular arc as a basis, the mid-point of which became the centre for a flatter section of greater radius, these two main parts being joined by shorter arcs of lesser radius. In addition the centres of these arcs were often set out using Pythagorean triangles or very close approximations thereto. Some basic mathematics show that for each Pythagorean triple (a,b,c) for which $a^2+b^2=c^2$, there exist two further quasi-Pythagorean triples for which $d^2+e^2=f^2+1$. With the latter, as numerical values increase, whilst Neolithic man may not have understood the algebraic side, he would have got an increasingly accurate right angle.

Flixton appears to be similarly set out starting with a 7,11,13 (quasi-Pythagorean) triangle, with radii for the semicircle of 11 units, the flat arc of 17 units and the joins of 4 units. However the whole appears then to have been stretched along the axis by a further 5 units so that it fits back around the original circle of radius 11 units. Taking these units as Thom's Megalithic Yard of 2.72 feet (829mm), a remarkably good fit is found for the sub-circle.

The plan of the post holes is encouragingly symmetrical, a flattened circle, which when taken along with a mirror image of itself and overlaid by eye can be seen to have a definite axis of symmetry in a roughly north-west to south-east direction passing through the positions of two internal post-holes and midway between two of the perimeter ones on the north-west side.

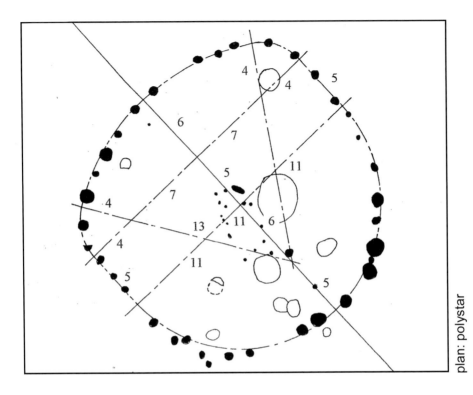

plan: polystar

Unfortunately the plan of the circle is now all we have to work on and the direction of the axis depends both on the accuracy of the archaeologist's survey and the effectiveness of the reflected overlay.

Calculating the direction of the axis from grid points traversed by it on the plan, to the north-west it lies 42.47° west of grid north, which is 39.75° west of true north, applying a 2.72° correction. It therefore has an azimuth value (measured clockwise from north) of 320.25° and corresponding amplitude (measured from west) of 50.25°.

The site is situated at latitude 52.42° north and in the direction of the axis the land rises from about 15 metres above OD on the flood plain to about 30 metres above OD at the valley side some 1.6 kilometres distant. This represents an altitude for the horizon in that direction of some 0.54°, which has to be adjusted downwards by 0.47° to account for astronomical refraction giving an adjusted altitude of 0.07°.

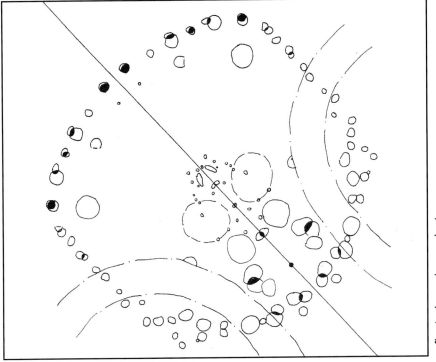

reflected overlay: polystar

Using Professor Thom's tables with these values for amplitude, latitude and altitude we can convert these figures to a declination for any celestial body setting along this axis of 28.02° from the equatorial plane. Around 2500 BC the moon would have had a maximum declination of 23.98 ±5.15°. These figures represent the angle of the ecliptic from the equator (earth's tilt towards the sun) and the additional angle added or subtracted between the moon's orbit and the ecliptic giving a maximum northwards setting for the moon when at declination 29.13°.

A further adjustment of 0.89° is then necessary to our declination to account for parallax, caused by the point of observation being on the earth's surface rather than at its centre, which is not negligible for relatively nearby bodies like the moon. This yields an expected declination for the moon's northernmost setting of 28.24°. Remarkably this lies within ¼° of the declination indicated by the axis of the post-hole circle, and even this small error can be removed if we allow a further ¼° of altitude to be added on, so that the alignment actually points to where the moon's lower limb would first touch the horizon as it sets.

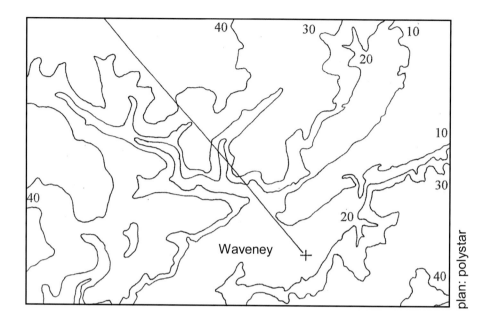

40   30   10
20
10
30
40
20
Waveney
40

plan: polystar

Looking along the axis from the rear of the enclosure, the two central posts framing the axis present about 4° of horizon, a comfortable space within which to view a moon of about ½° width. In addition to the motions already described the moon's orbit has a further wobble of ±0.15°, the so called minor perturbation, which, if detected, would enable eclipses to be predicted.

The use of additional foresights, or as has been proposed for many a stone circle, the use of a topographical notch on the horizon, could greatly assist the accuracy of lunar observations and permit detection of this wobble.

Flixton appears to have been sited with such a topographical notch in mind, for to the north-west the horizon does dip noticeably along the line of a small tributary joining the Waveney from the north. This provides a dip of about 0.3° between about 57° and 44° west of grid north and was probably the best that could be achieved in such unhilly country.

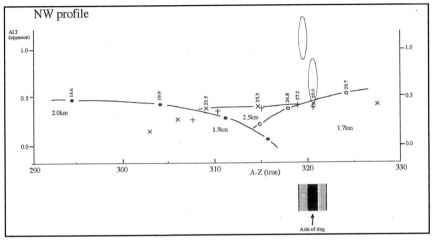

In 2006 Ruggles' report to Suffolk County Council agreed with the author's contention that the monument was set out aligned on an axis of symmetry pointing at the moon's northernmost setting point, however he does not consider that the site was a lunar observatory!

As part of his investigation, Ruggles also looked at a potential cross axis to the monument. He concluded that whilst a second axis perpendicular to the main one might exist, it was about 3° out from the point at which the sun would rise at its maximum northwards position, on the summer solstice.

This proposed cross axis was also about twice as much out in relation to the position of the long barrow (LB) further south on the horizon and therefore it seems a lost cause.

However by superimposing the actual position of the midsummer sunrise on his diagram (see overleaf), we can see that there is in fact an alignment in this rough direction. The monument has been sited so that at midsummer, the sunrise would graze up the valley side, much as Thom found for many a Scottish stone circle. The rest of the year the sun would rise further south, always off the higher land.

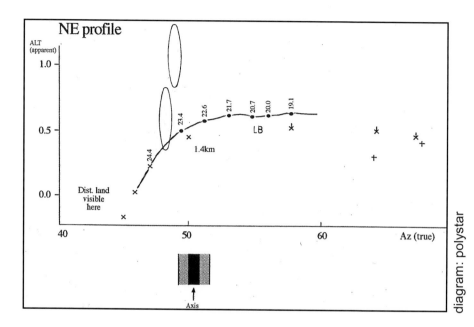

In conclusion then we seem to have a set of post-holes at Flixton, whose plan geometry appears to match that of many stone circles, using the same unit of measurement as proposed by Thom. Its geometrical symmetry identifies an axis to the north-west where the moon sets at its maximum northwards declination.

The circle also seems to have been sited so that this axis lies over a tributary valley to the north-west, providing a topographical sight line in that direction. Relative to another almost perpendicular axis a second topographical sight line identifies the sun rising at its maximum northwards declination, grazing up the side of the main river valley.

Basically the evidence at Flixton is as good as at many a stone circle, and if Thom is right then other similar sites on the eastern side of the country, not previously considered in this way, are now eminently suitable for further investigation.

It is perhaps to be regretted that such finds as this circle and its adjoining long barrow have been excavated prior to gravel extraction works, which have now eradicated them forever, leaving us with only a paper memory of their former existence.

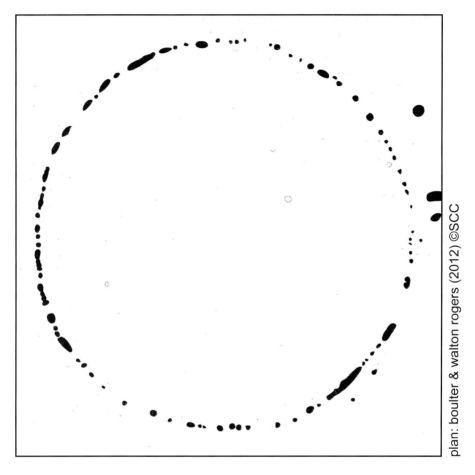

plan: boulter & walton rogers (2012) ©SCC

Since 1997, the excavations at Flixton have proceeded apace keeping just ahead of the excavator buckets of the gravel extractors. To the north-east of the timber circle site a further timber circle was discovered, shown at 1:133 above and in its context overleaf. This was found to be Iron Age or early Roman in date and described as a palisaded circle, presumably used for keeping stock. The use of halved timbers packed close together is reminiscent of the circle at Holme-next-the-Sea, however the scale of it is altogether different, at some 27 metres in diameter it is half as big again as the nearby timber circle, and four times the size of Holme.

Later still in 2010 two further circles of timber post-holes were reported, 12 and 13.5 metres in diameter respectively, both with central pits containing burials, the larger one with two ditches around the perimeter. Publication of these recent finds is awaited with interest.

REFERENCES

Boulter, S. 1998 *Flixton Park, Flixton*
                          Suffolk CC Archaeological Report 97/53

Boulter, S. & Walton Rogers, P. 2012 *Circles and Cemeteries: Excavations
                          at Flixton Volume 1* East Anglian Archaeology 147

Dymond, D. & Martin, E. (eds) 1999 *An Historical Atlas of Suffolk*
                          Suffolk CC / SIAH

Gibson, A. 1998 *Stonehenge & Timber Circles* Tempus

Ruggles, C. 1999 *Astronomy in Prehistoric Britain and Ireland* Yale UP

Ruggles, C. 2006 *Astronomical Potential of the Flixton Timber Circle*
                          Report for Suffolk CC

Taylor, P. 2009 *Flixton: Neolithic Lunar Observatory* Polystar Press

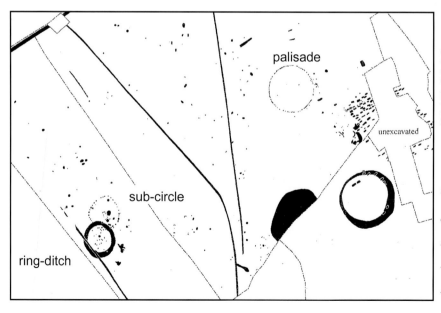

plan: boulter & walton rogers (2012) ©SCC

INTRODUCTION

photo: mark brennand, ©NAU

The timber circle discovered on the beach at Holme-next-the-Sea in 1998 is neither circular nor strictly the same as other timber circles. Because they do not last, the latter are relatively uncommon (or at least undiscovered) in the east, mostly consisting of rings of timber post holes set some distance apart, very much the timber counterparts of the stone circles found more commonly in the west and north of Britain.

Since the circle at Holme has been loosely classified by the archaeologists in the 'timber circle' category, probably for lack of anything else quite like it, we will examine the remains at Holme as such, but under a much broader interpretation, that of Neolithic circles in general. Stone circles were studied extensively by Alexander Thom in the 1960's and he claimed to find in them evidence of geometrical setting out using a standard unit of length, the Megalithic Yard (2.72 feet or 829mm).

Thom also found impressive astronomical orientations suggesting intimate knowledge of the finer motions of the moon, such as would make eclipse prediction quite feasible. Following on from the author's discovery of a lunar alignment at the Flixton timber circle in north Suffolk, this paper sought evidence for Thom's claims in another of the timber circles then coming to light in the east. Unlike the Flixton case it was not however taken up by the archaeologists.

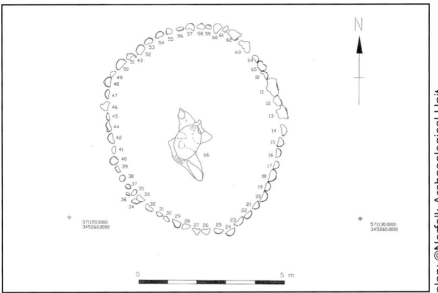

plan: ©Norfolk Archaeological Unit

We have at Holme (TF 711452) a timber construction in an area not known for its stone. Hardwood presents a fairly durable alternative to stone, easily worked whilst green and probably in plentiful supply locally. The monument is near water where we find the majority of our Neolithic sites, perhaps indicative of its being simply an eastern counterpart of the western remains from the water-borne 'megalithic' culture.

The Holme circle has been dated to 2049 BC and comes a little late in the overall scheme of these essentially Neolithic monuments, but that may well explain its difference from the main run of such sites. Rather than the 'circle' of discrete post holes, such as was found at Flixton in north Suffolk, or Arminghall near Norwich, we have here essentially a 'circular' trench filled with 56 butted together half trees with their bark still on and facing outwards.

We know all this because here the timbers have come down to us intact in their lower portions at least, as has the unusual upturned tree bole found inside the circle. Stone circles do occasionally have similar 'inliers', e.g. Boscawen Un circle in west Cornwall has a single leaning monolith (see p.5), whilst the Mayburgh Henge in Cumberland had several standing stones inside a large circular ditched monument, of which but one remains.

photo: polystar

The Time Team replica

photo: polystar

Signs of rot, 2008

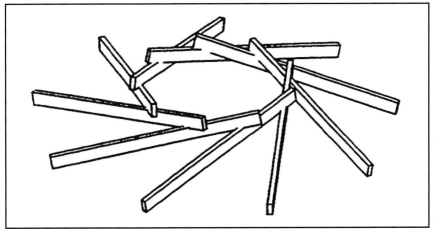

diagram: polystar

Reciprocal frame

It would seem that the sea has been both the circle's salvation and its nemesis. The replica circle built by the Time Team in the winter of 1999/2000 in a similar setting to the original about a mile inland was by 2008 already showing severe signs of decay above ground. Whilst this was an interesting and valid exercise in experimental archaeology, doubtless very useful in determining the techniques for building such a circle, there does not seem to have been any follow up.

The replica now seems forlorn and forgotten, but the story continues to unfold and the timbers there have suffered extensive beetle attack and are showing signs of fungal rot at ground level, such that not much will remain in another ten years. The buried bases of the timbers may last longer as they did in the original, which is presumed to have been covered for some considerable time by sand dunes moving slowly inland, until they eventually reappeared exposed on the beach as a result of tidal action.

This suggests that the circle may be no more than a temporary structure, used for a few years, rather than a 'monument' meant to last forever. The laying out of bodies on the upturned stump for excarnation seems a likely function one might screen with a timber wall in this way. If this is what it was for, then the larger bones were probably removed to somewhere else for storage once devoid of flesh. The notion of a tribal centre based at a circular monument with a distant but visible tomb for the ancestors on nearby higher ground is a model that might fit here.

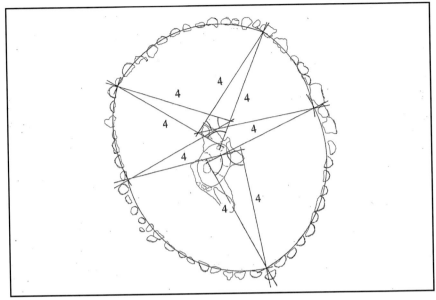

plan: polystar

The problem at Holme is that we have a good plan, but no evidence of anything in three dimensions. The replica assumes a wall of barked timbers was the external elevation, a simple projection of the plan into a third dimension. We do not know whether it had earth banked against it, whether it had a roof structure or even whether it was buried completely.

The same questions are often asked about the megalithic quoits in the far west of Britain. One possibility with such a curtain wall of timbers is a reciprocal frame type of roof, where each rafter sits on one adjoining rafter and in turn supports the next. Such a structure is essentially free standing with little tendency to spread and would leave a circular hole in the centre through which the agents of excarnation could easily gain access.

In relation to the other monuments with which it is loosely classified, it is very small at roughly 6x7 metres in diameter, as can be seen at 1:200 on this section's frontispiece. An accurate plan of the Holme circle reveals it not to be an actual circle, but almost boat-shaped like a large coracle.

Thom has shown that egg-shaped enclosures are not unusual amongst stone circles and using his Megalithic Yard as a unit, the shape can be set out to a good approximation by a series of five arcs of radius 4 Megalithic Yards, all centred on the central tree stump area, but it is not quite one of his type I eggs.

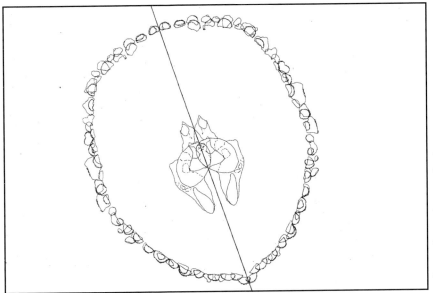

reflected overlay: polystar

The plan appears to have an axis of symmetry, which can be better identified by superimposing a reflected overlay and finding a best fit by eye. This axis points out to the NNW across the sea of the Wash at an angle 19.61° west of grid north, i.e. 17.46° west of true north. The axis thus has an amplitude, measured from true west, of 72.54°. The site is at latitude 52.98°N and the northern horizon presents zero altitude, which when adjusted for astronomical refraction gives an adjusted altitude of -0.55°.

Taking these values of amplitude, latitude and altitude we can apply them to Professor Thom's tables to derive the declination for any celestial body setting at this point on the north western horizon. The resulting declination is 34.47°, way beyond the northern limit of the sun (23.9°) and even the moon (29.1°). The only other possibility might be a bright star, but none present themselves in this area of declination at a date 2000 BC.

If we look back along the axis, inland to the SSE, things show slightly more promise. Directly along the line it passes over the westernmost of two hillocks approximately 1 kilometre apart (the eastern one is known as Beacon Hill). These are probably the only noticeable local topographical features in the landscape thereabouts, although from the circle site they are now obscured by sand dunes. Intervisibility can however be confirmed, for from the hilltop the dunes can clearly be seen, just left of a tree belt around the RSPB headquarters.

HOLME INLAND

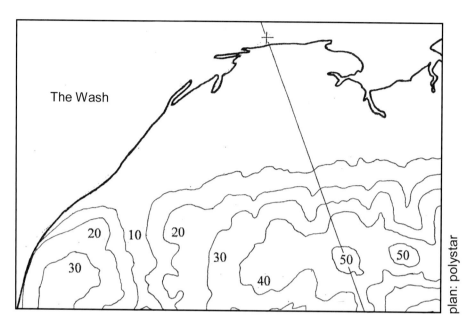

The Wash

plan: polystar

Axis inland over hill

drawing: polystar

Aerial photo of hilltop

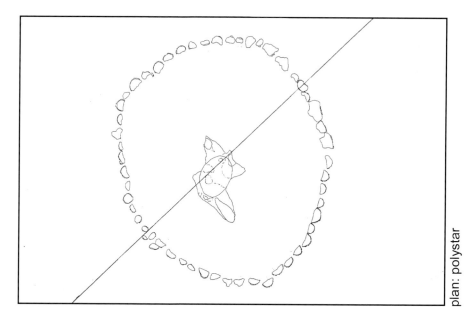

plan: polystar

Both hills are 50 metres high at a distance of 3.5 kilometres from the timber circle, giving an altitude for the horizon along the axis of 0.82°, which when adjusted for refraction gives us 0.39°. Again using Thom's tables we get a declination for any celestial body rising along this line of -34.63°.

Even with the added altitude, this declination is nowhere near the sun or even the moon at its maximum southwards. Unfortunately since Thom did most of his work based around Scottish sites, he did not consider declinations less than -30° as these would not ever be visible at latitudes greater than 60°N.

Aerial photographs of the western hilltop appear to show some form of disturbance along the axis in the centre of the hilltop field between the more obvious tractor turn marks at either side. Such cropmarks are often good clues to archaeology and perhaps should be investigated. If this turns out to be where the bones were taken, then the axis is explained.

The only other point of minor consequence here is that this inland alignment is about one mile east of and virtually parallel to the northern section of the Peddar's Way, the ancient track-way from inland to the Wash that later became a Roman road. Most of the landscape features hereabouts follow a grid pattern, parallel to both the shore and this route perpendicular to it.

A SOLAR ALIGNMENT?

photo: polystar

One other possible alignment is suggested by both the geometry of the circle and the local topography. Post 65 on the north-eastern side of the circle appears to be special as the only unsplit single post there with bark all around it. Looking south-westwards across the centre of the circle over the upturned bole, we find posts 35 and 37, also seemingly intact, but this pair are thought to form the entrance as they are conjoined below ground level.

This 'entrance' frames a view to the south-west passing over low ground to where Old Hunstanton now stands, presenting us with perhaps the most prominent landscape feature in the locality, the end of the cliffs, where land 30m high suddenly stops, nowadays marked by a lighthouse near the edge.

Through this entrance gap the alignment is 47.64° from grid south, i.e. 49.68° from true south. This has an azimuth of 229.68°, giving an amplitude of -40.32°. Over the cliff top the altitude is 0.25°, which has to be adjusted downwards 0.51° for refraction to give -0.26°.

By again applying Thom's table we obtain a declination for the setting of a heavenly body along this line of -23.14°. This is comfortably near the sun's minimum declination in 2000 BC of -23.93°, and allowing for the ½° width of the sun's disc, even nearer the declination of its upper limb at this time, some -23.68°.

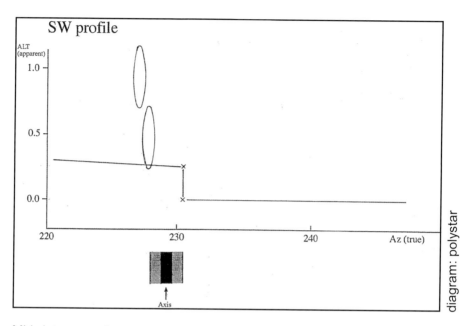

Midwinter sunset

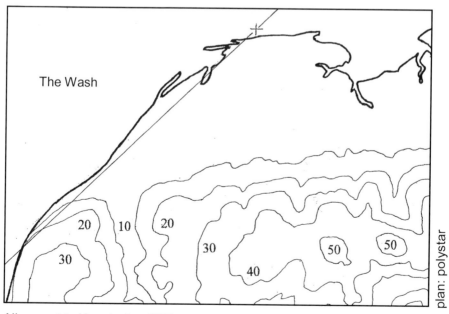

Alignment to Hunstanton Cliffs

TO SUMMARISE

photo: polystar

The circle's axis of symmetry seems to point one way NNW out to sea, the other way to the nearby hill to the SSE, but for no apparent astronomical reason. Some investigation of what might lie hidden on top of that hill, may throw further light on the matter.

Otherwise from the foregoing it seems likely that the Holme circle may have been set out geometrically and more likely that it was sited so that the cliff at Hunstanton caught the sun setting at its maximum southwards declination. For most of the year the sun would always set into the sea in the west or north-west.

However for a few days at the winter solstice, the sun would rise off the land to the south-east and set again into the land of the clifftops to the south-west. A few days later its setting would creep back northwards, the first sign of the return of light and start of a new year being the re-appearance of glowing embers at the foot of the cliff a short while after the sun had seemingly set.

The above photograph of an actual sunset was taken at 3.35pm on 21 December 2008, showing the phenomenon at its extreme position. The series of pictures was of necessity taken from a position on the dunes (approx TF 706448) on the line between the circle site and the cliff, 600 metres from the former but still a distance of some 4 kilometres from the cliff.

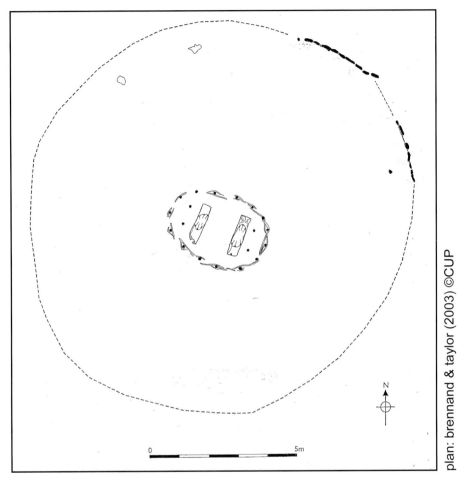

plan: brennand & taylor (2003) ©CUP

Known by the archaeologists as 'Holme II', a second timber structure believed to be roughly circular was found on the same beach about 100 metres east of 'Seahenge', as shown above at a scale of 1:125. It has a diameter of some 13 metres, about twice the size of Seahenge, and appears to have been constructed at exactly the same date and in a similar way using split oak timbers.

There is a smaller elliptical central structure of woven twig-work containing what appear to be two platforms suitably body sized, which may represent a continuation of the use thought likely for Seahenge itself. An arc of about one sixth of the perimeter was apparent as eroded timber stumps at the time of the Seahenge excavations (see photo overleaf), and by now much more may well be visible as the sea takes its toll.

REFERENCES

Ashwin, T. & Davison, A. 2005 *An Historical Atlas of Norfolk* Phillimore

Brennand, M. & Taylor, M. 2003 *The Survey and Excavation of a Bronze Age Timber Circle at Holme-next-the-Sea, Norfolk 1998-9* Proceedings of the Prehistoric Society vol.69 pp.1-84 Cambridge UP

Gibson, A. 1998 *Stonehenge & Timber Circles* Tempus

Pitts, M. 2000 *Hengeworld* Arrow

Pryor, F. 2001 *Seahenge* Harper Collins

Taylor, P. 2009 *Seahenge: Sun Sand and Winter Solstice* Polystar Press

photo: brennand & taylor (2003) ©CUP

Holme II

ARMINGHALL: WOODHENGE OF THE EAST

photo: clark (1936) crown copyright

Probably the earliest discovery of a timber circle in the eastern counties, the 'henge' at Arminghall (TG 240060), just south of Norwich, is far from typical. It was discovered by aerial photography in 1929 by Wing Commander Gilbert Insall VC, who had previously found the concentric timber circles in Wiltshire, now known as Woodhenge. Indeed, had he not found that first, it seems likely that epithet would have been much more aptly applied to the Arminghall monument.

The monument consisted of a horseshoe shaped array of eight large timber posts open to the south-west, with a pair of circular ditches outside it separated by a bank. The inner ditch is interrupted by a causeway entrance on the south-west side, as may have been the outer ditch. Unfortunately this remains unknown as the latter is incomplete in this sector, interrupted by a field boundary.

The parallels with Stonehenge, where the horseshoe is open to the north-east and the site oriented towards midsummer sunrise, lead one to think this site may well be oriented in the opposite direction towards midwinter sunset. It seems not unreasonable therefore to investigate this monument using the methods applied by Professor Alexander Thom in the 1960's and 1970's to both Stonehenge and many other stone circles to see whether there is any evidence of geometrical setting out or indeed astronomical alignments in this monument.

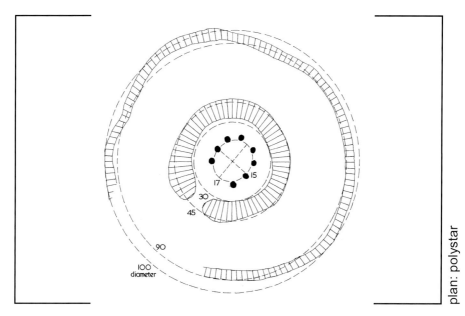

plan: polystar

Looking at the overall plan of the monument, the eight posts can be considered as sitting around an ellipse (a = 4, b = 7.5, c = 8.5) with short and long diameters of 15 and 17 Megalithic Yards respectively. This unit of measurement was found by Thom to have been used in the setting out of many stone circles across the British Isles and there is no reason to think it would not be used here. This accords well with North's observation (1996) that the inner ditch sits between two concentric circles of 30 and 45 Megalithic Yards diameter and the outer ditch fits roughly within a circle of 100 Megalithic Yards diameter. This last could equally be considered as lying for the most part outside a circle of 90 Megalithic Yards diameter.

The horseshoe shaped layout has obvious parallels with Stonehenge and has led to speculations whether the posts might have had lintels as they do at that monument. This may have been in pairs as in the central horseshoe at Stonehenge, or maybe continuously as in the outer circle.

The posts themselves are believed to have been stripped of bark and showed some signs of burning, although this may have been a result of the felling process (luckily the charcoal has given us a date of 3100 BC for the monument). The posts were set some six feet or more into the ground and were in the region of 2'6" to 3'0" in diameter (roughly a Megalithic Yard!). Comparison with the structure of a timber-framed house is enough to confirm that they would have adequately carried the load of timber lintels up to twenty feet long.

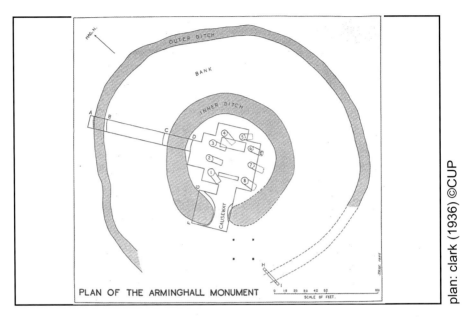

PLAN OF THE ARMINGHALL MONUMENT

plan: clark (1936) ©CUP

Although the symmetry of the plan is very obvious with a distinct south-west to north-east axis, the problem comes when trying to assess the exact direction in which this points. Two clues are given us in the published details of the excavation carried out by Grahame Clark in 1935.

The first of these is a 'magnetic north' point shown on the plan, a notoriously variable direction, which in 1935 was somewhere between 10° and 15° west of true north, but may have been quite variable locally with the presence of both the pylon and the overhead high voltage cables it carried. The second clue is the pylon itself, the feet of which were used as setting out points for the grid on which the archaeological information was mapped. Its plotted position on the plan relative to the monument is thus unlikely to be inaccurate, however that pylon has now been replaced by two others, spaced either side of the original site.

Fortunately all is not lost and the direction of the axis can be confirmed by reference to the line of White Horse Lane, south of the monument, visible on both old and new aerial photographs, allowing the site plan to be rectified to modern maps. Beex and Peterson (2004) have carried out the necessary mapwork and obtained by means of mirror symmetry an axis for the monument of 40.5° east of grid north. Applying a 2.63° correction to this axis gives the direction as 43.13° east of true north, so that it has amplitude, measured from true east, of 46.87°.

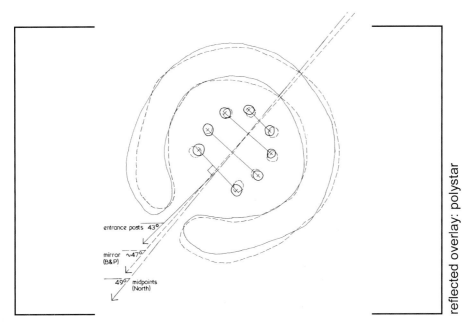

entrance posts 43°

mirror ~47°
(B&P)

49° midpoints
(North)

reflected overlay: polystar

Beex and Peterson's axis is at least central to the 'causeway' entrance, but differs a little from the approximate 43° amplitude of any midsummer sunrise / midwinter sunset line at this latitude. It also differs from North's 1996 estimate of 41.0° amplitude (given as south of west), which they claim was miscalculated and unreliable. It seems likely that North's angle should simply have been given as 'west of south' which would give an amplitude of 49.0°, a little to the south of Beex and Peterson's axis.

So obvious is the symmetry of the Arminghall henge that using a reflected overlay to find an axis might seem superfluous. It is however instructive as it shows that the axis obtained by this method (Beex and Peterson) is indeed nearer west than that obtained by taking midpoints between pairs of posts (North as corrected). It also shows that whilst the three north-eastern pairs of post-holes do indeed reflect fairly accurately across the centre, the south-western pair at the entrance to the horseshoe is a little twisted off axis. The line through these two posts' midpoints is approximately 43° west of true north, so that a notional perpendicular facing out of the horseshoe entrance takes a line 43° south of west, directly towards midwinter sunset.

So what lies between 40° and 50° south of west as seen from the Arminghall henge? The answer is the most significant local landscape feature for miles around, providing a well defined lump on the horizon when seen from the monument.

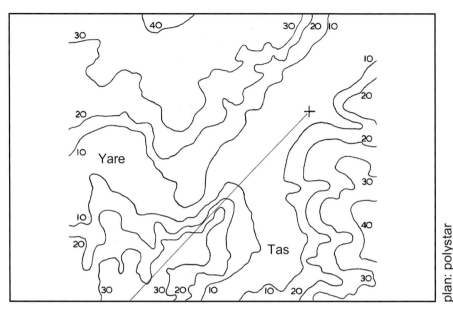

plan: polystar

Chapel Hill, carved out of the Norfolk landscape by the Rivers Tas and Yare that meet just west of the monument, was undoubtedly important to our ancestors. Its summit is the site of a Bronze Age barrow cemetery around what was later Harford Farm. Excavated in 1990, prior to being swept away for the Norwich southern by-pass, about half a dozen ring ditches were found. Perhaps more important to the present exercise, the Arminghall symmetry axis, given by Beex and Peterson at 46.87° south of west, passes right through the area.

Seen from the Arminghall monument, this axis runs a little south of the apparent summit of Chapel Hill, whilst the line of midwinter sunset is a little nearer west with an amplitude 42.95° south of west. This would make the sun effectively roll down the northern flank of the hill as it sets at its furthest south on the midwinter solstice. This direction can be confirmed by using Thom's table with latitude of 52.6° north and aiming for the sun's minimum declination of -24.05° in 3100 BC, the date given by radiocarbon analysis of the charcoal.

The top of Chapel Hill is 36 metres above Ordnance Datum, some 32 metres above the monument at approximately 4 metres. This gives an altitude for the horizon over the hill some 2 kilometres distant as 0.92°, which has to be adjusted downwards by 0.47° to account for atmospheric refraction giving an apparent altitude of 0.45°.

photo: clark (1936) crown copyright

A little nearer west than the line towards midwinter sunset from the Arminghall monument, there is another significant circular monument at approximately TG 233053. Just across the River Tas in the parish of Markshall, an aerial photograph of this second circle was shown in the original Arminghall paper (Plate II) and marked therein on a map (Fig. 2) as location B. Not much was made of it at the time and to this day it remains unexcavated, which seems surprising as from the initial evidence of the aerial photographs it looks equally interesting.

Like Arminghall it is a Scheduled Monument, but this has done little to protect it from the plough, such that now it is only just visible in aerial photographs. It should really either be dug before it is completely destroyed by ploughing or fenced off and saved for future archaeological investigation.

This circular monument at Markshall can still be traced on modern aerial photographs and mainly comprises a pair of concentric circles. The outer cropmark, probably a ditch, is between 35 and 40 Megalithic Yards in diameter, whilst the inner ring seems to contain some post-holes and is about 15 Megalithic Yards in diameter. These dimensions are roughly the same as those found for the centre line of the inner ditch and post-hole horseshoe respectively at Arminghall. Just to the west of the Markshall circle a further cropmark outlines a large area within a D-shaped boundary, which may or may not be connected with the circle, and there is something of a halo, particularly to the north which might be a large outer ditch.

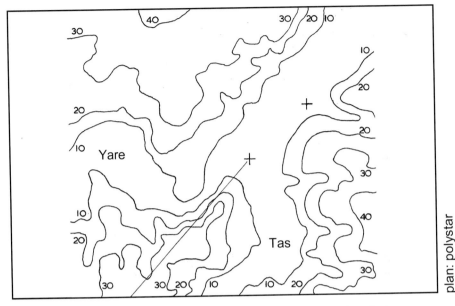

plan: polystar

In the absence of further archaeological evidence for the time being, we can at least look at this second circle in its landscape context.

Like the Arminghall circle, the Markshall one is also situated on the gravel shelf on the south-east side of the River Yare. However Markshall is just upstream of the junction with the River Tas, and thus on spur of gravel that juts out into the confluence of the two rivers.

Looking towards Chapel Hill from the Markshall circle, the altitude of the horizon is greater since the hill is about a kilometre nearer, so the result we will get from a declination of -24.05° will be a little nearer south, and thus likely to still be over the hill.

If we again use Thom's tables, we are still at latitude 52.6° north, but now the altitude is 1.83°, which as before has to be adjusted downwards by 0.47° to account for astronomical refraction giving an adjusted altitude of 1.36°. The sun at its minimum declination of -24.05° in 3100 BC would thus have set at amplitude 44.55° south of west.

A little bit of trigonometry can show that this line crosses the midwinter sunset line from Arminghall about a further kilometre south-west of the Markshall monument, pretty much right on the northern flank of Chapel Hill.

photo: polystar

The outcome of all this is that we seem to have the same view of the midwinter solstice sunset from both monuments. The sun is seen to come in low over the hilltop and then disappears gradually down the northern flank of Chapel Hill. The photograph above was taken from the road roughly midway between the two sites on 17 December 2010, four days before the solstice and shows to good effect what would have been seen from either of these monuments in 3100 BC at the winter solstice.

The only slight difference between the two sites would be one of timing, as counter-intuitively the sun would appear to set about seven minutes earlier at the more westerly Markshall site. A loud noise made at that time would easily be heard at the more easterly site, where the event would be rerun a little later. Indeed a good runner could effectively make the sun 'stand still' and witness the event at both sites.

So, is this second pair of concentric circles at Markshall, about 1,000 metres to the south-west, in fact the other end of the same monument? Is Markshall in fact the 'Stonehenge' to Arminghall's 'Woodhenge'? In comparison the Thornborough henges in north Yorkshire comprise three large circular banked enclosures set about 750 metres apart along a line running north-west to south-east. The Sanctuary in north Wiltshire is set some 2,000 metres south-east of the Avebury circle and Woodhenge in south Wiltshire is about 3,000 metres north-east of Stonehenge.

photo: polystar

What is really needed to answer these questions is a dig at the Markshall site, the landscape evidence is there, but the presence or otherwise of post-holes laid out in some recognizable pattern, perhaps with a significant axis of symmetry would determine the matter.

As we have seen the timber setting at Arminghall is not exactly a timber circle, but it was made of timber and set within two circular ditches. The nearby circle at Markshall may still conceal a timber circle or setting of some kind, but only excavation is going to settle the matter.

Although both these sites have thus far had little to offer in terms of geometric setting out, as with many a stone circle, it seems likely that both monuments' sites were chosen to take advantage of the topography. Their positioning in the landscape appears significant, both relating to midwinter sunset over the same landscape feature.

Whilst Professor Thom's theories may currently be given short shrift in the archaeological world, their application here points to the need for perhaps a little more work to be done in the field. If this is indeed a major ceremonial site, it is perhaps the only one we have here in the eastern counties and is all the more valuable for that.

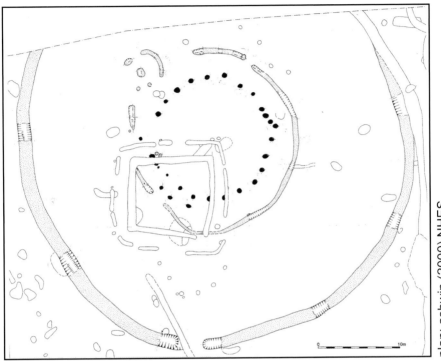

plan: ashwin (2000) NHES

Whilst the two sites at Arminghall and Markshall seem to be orientated towards the northern flank of Chapel Hill, where the midwinter sun sets, there is on the southern flank a further site of interest excavated in 1990 just prior to the building of Norwich's southern by-pass. The axis of the horseshoe at Arminghall as given by Beex & Peterson aligns with a site containing a series of ring-ditches at Harford Farm, which proved to be a Bronze Age barrow cemetery (TG 224043).

Amongst these there are two circles of timber posts that may have been there to retain a mound or may have been free-standing timber circles. The northernmost of these was essentially free-standing, not related to any particular ring-ditch, and is thought to be a Bronze Age round-house, obviously with a roof at some time.

As shown above, the southernmost one is sited within two concentric ditches and is described by the archaeologists as a 'hengiform barrow', although no traces remain of any mound, suggesting that this circle of timbers was also probably free-standing.

71

REFERENCES

Ashwin, T. 2000 *Excavations at Harford Farm, Caistor St Edmund, 1990*
East Anglian Archaeology 91

Ashwin, T. & Davison, A. 2005 *An Historical Atlas of Norfolk* Phillimore

Beex, W. & Peterson, J. 2004 *The Arminghall Henge in Space and Time*
BAR International 1227

Clark, G. 1936 *The Timber Monument at Arminghall and its Affinities*
Proceedings of the Prehistoric Society vol 2 pp.1-51 Cambridge UP

Gibson, A. 1998 *Stonehenge & Timber Circles* Tempus

North, J. 1996 *Stonehenge: Neolithic Man and the Cosmos* HarperCollins

Pitts, M. 2000 *Hengeworld* Arrow

Taylor, P. 2011 *Arminghall: Woodhenge of the East* Polystar Press

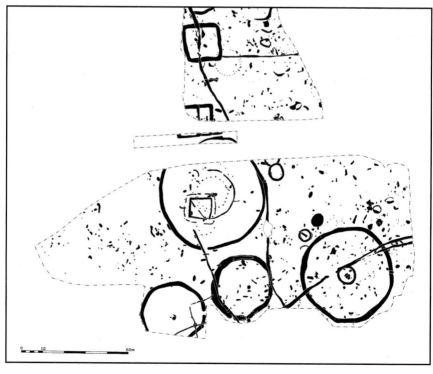

plan: ashwin (2000) NHES

LAWFORD: A TIMBER CIRCLE OVERLOOKED

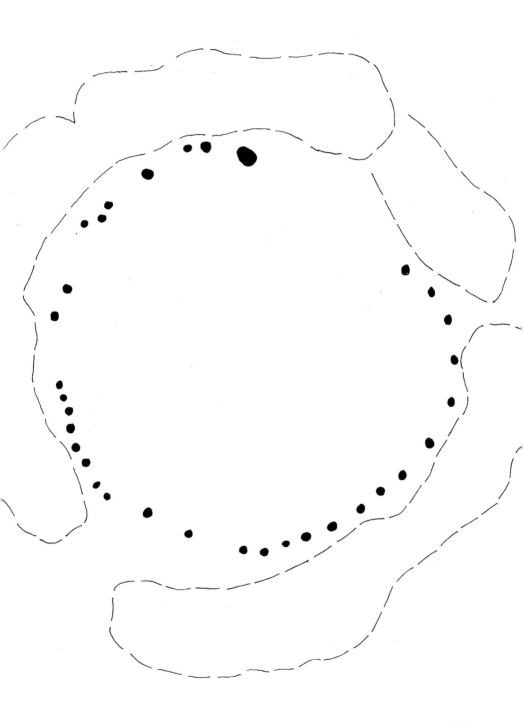

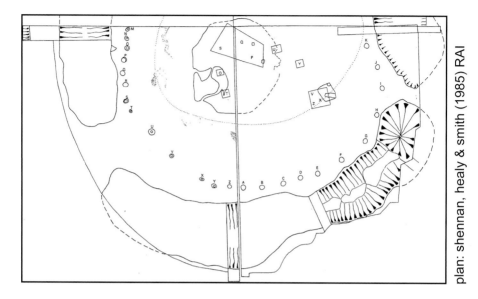

plan: shennan, healy & smith (1985) RAI

Having found a significant lunar alignment and some interesting geometry in the setting out of the timber circle site at Flixton in north Suffolk, it seemed sensible to examine a number of other similar sites in the east of England with a view to discovering further evidence of our Neolithic ancestors' abilities in these matters.

Professor Alexander Thom's pioneering work on stone circles in the 1960's claimed to find evidence of geometrical setting out using a standard unit of length, the Megalithic Yard (2.72 feet or 829mm). Thom also found impressive astronomical orientations suggesting intimate knowledge of the finer motions of the moon, such as would make eclipse prediction feasible.

His theories were rigorously opposed by the archaeological fraternity at the time because they would deny the long held belief that innovation always came to this country by diffusion from the east, where there were supposedly higher civilizations. Fortunately radiocarbon dating eventually put paid to their theories on this, showing that many things were actually here first, but Thom got a raw deal and died without his ideas ever being properly revisited.

If we can find evidence for his claims in the timber circles now coming to light in the east, it could mean that Thom was right. This short paper therefore seeks to amass further evidence by looking at another possible site, a nearly circular setting of post-holes within a ring ditch in north-east Essex at Lawford (TM 088309).

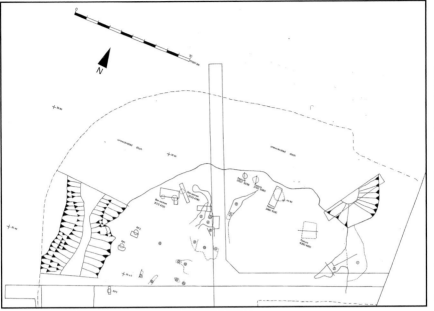

plan: shennan, healy & smith (1985) RAI

The ring ditch was excavated in two main phases in 1962/3 and 1971, the results not coming to publication until 1985. The first phase dealt with the southern half of the site only, the second phase took on the rest and revisited some of the first area.

The first excavator was of the opinion that the site was essentially domestic in nature, there being a large patch of black burnt material near the centre, but nothing to indicate a hut or any such over it. The whole area was later buried by a small mound created by the digging of a ditch around it. The semi-circle of small holes just within the ditch, he took to be for posts for a fence to retain the mound.

The later excavators thought the black area was more likely a midden, and seem to have found relatively fewer remains of the post-hole circle in the northern half of the site, assuming that perhaps the evidence for these had been lost to deep ploughing or that the first excavator had been mistaken!

The published paper on the site has little to say about the circle of post-holes, and seems to expend an inordinate amount of energy on pottery and flint classification and the nature of the ditch fill with its many coloured sands and clays. The plans appear in two separate halves, with much detail of the ditch profile, such that the two half circles of posts seem merely coincidental.

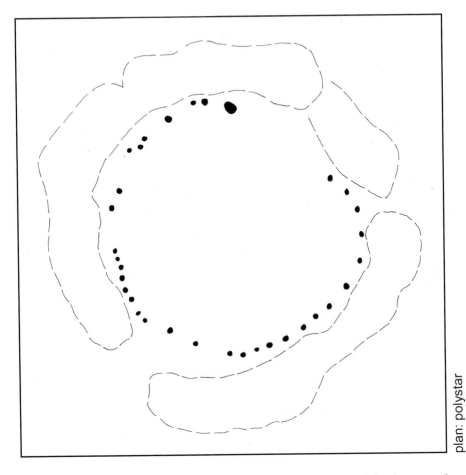

plan: polystar

As they are not seen together on the same page in the published paper, the two halves of the plan are not appreciated there for what they might represent. Assembling them is quite revelatory, but not without its difficulties. The two plans do dovetail together fairly well when copied at the same scale, but unfortunately their north points do not quite coincide, an oversight that is regrettable when wanting to carry out any sort of astronomical investigation for the site.

It seems likely that the later north point is the more accurate as it is accompanied by a grid covering the site, but no clue is given in the text as to which north (magnetic, grid or true) we are witnessing. The 'circle' once assembled is found to be actually flattened on the north-east side, of a shape not unlike that at Flixton or indeed many a stone circle, and in size slightly larger than Flixton, about midway in the range found for stone circles.

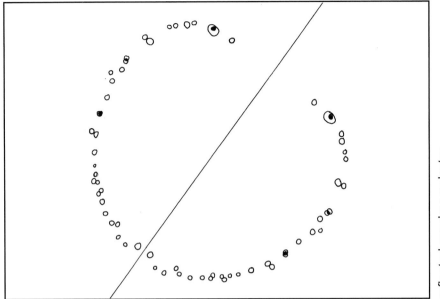

reflected overlay: polystar

Interestingly the main gap in the ditch is on the south-west side opposite the flattening, representing perhaps a main approach to the circle. One other much smaller gap in the ditch had been detected on the east side, but might represent poor workmanship as the ditch is believed to have been dug as a series of joined up pits.

Overall the circle presents us with an underlying north-east / south-west axis of symmetry, which will bear some further investigation. Although there is a paucity of post-holes around the northern half of the circle (the later excavation), there are two fairly well defined 'shoulders' where the flattened north-eastern section joins the main 'circular' perimeter. These irregularities will be found very useful in what follows.

As was found helpful at Flixton, superimposing a reflected image of the plan allows the two sets of post-holes to be aligned to a best fit by eye, without the need to resort to any complicated algebraic geometry or statistical analysis.

This best fit thus provides an axis for the monument, which can then be examined for any possible astronomical significance. Assuming the grid given in the later excavation is in fact grid north, this axis turns out to be 36.50° east of grid north, which applying a 2.37° correction is 38.87° east of true north. It thus has an amplitude, measured from true east of 51.13°.

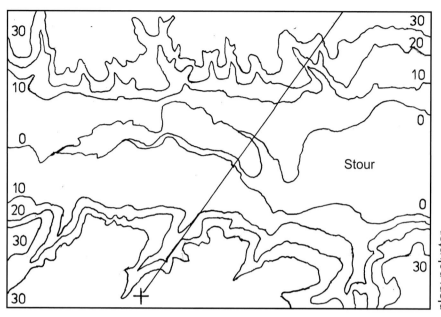

plan: polystar

The site is situated at latitude 51.94° north and in the direction of the axis the land is basically level, rising on both sides of the river from sea level to just over 30 metres above OD, both at the site and on the opposite bank where the village of Brantham can be found. This represents an altitude for the horizon in that direction of 0.00°, which has to be adjusted downwards by 0.47° to account for astronomical refraction to an adjusted altitude of -0.47°.

Using Professor Thom's tables with these values for amplitude, latitude and altitude we can convert these figures to a declination for any celestial body rising along this axis of 28.25° from the equatorial plane. Around 2500 BC the moon would have had a declination of 23.98 ±5.15°. These figures represent the angle of the ecliptic from the equator (earth's tilt towards the sun) and the additional angle added or subtracted between the moon's orbit and the ecliptic giving a maximum northwards rising for the moon when at declination 29.13°.

A further adjustment of 0.89° is then necessary to account for parallax, caused by the point of observation being on the earth's surface rather than at its centre, which is not negligible for relatively nearby bodies like the moon. This yields an expected declination for the moon's northernmost rising of 28.24°. This lies remarkably close to the declination indicated by the axis of the post-hole circle. It should not be forgotten however that this axis has been based on a best fit by eye reflected overlay and on the archaeologists' north point being grid north.

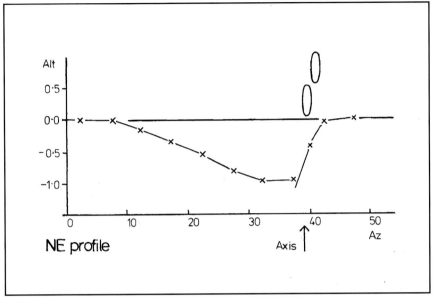

NE profile — Alt / Az axis diagram. diagram: polystar

Looking along the axis from the south-western entrance into the enclosure, two central posts on the opposite flattened north-eastern section could easily have framed a stretch of a few degrees of horizon, within which the motions of a moon of about ½° width could be comfortably observed. Unfortunately, unlike Flixton, this is the precise area at Lawford where we have no surviving evidence for posts, but then as we know in archaeology, absence of evidence is not necessarily evidence of absence.

In addition to the motions already described the moon's orbit has a further wobble of ±0.15°, the so called minor perturbation, which, if detected, would enable eclipses to be predicted. The use of additional foresights, or as has been proposed for many a stone circle, the use of a topographical notch on the horizon, could greatly assist the accuracy of lunar observations and permit detection of this wobble.

Lawford appears to have been sited with such a topographical notch in mind. Whilst to the north-east the distant horizon over the river does not dip appreciably, there is nearer the monument along the axis the line of a small tributary joining the Stour from the south. This provides a maximum dip of about 0.9° between about 30° and 35° east of grid north and would have made the moon at its maximum appear to come out of this river valley.

A FLATTENED CIRCLE

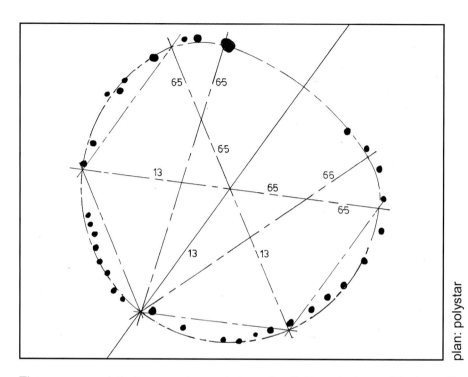

plan: polystar

Thom proposed that many stone circles of a flattened shape (his type A) were set out using a two-thirds circular arc as a basis, the mid-point of which became the centre for a flatter section of greater radius, these two main parts being joined by shorter arcs of half the original circle's radius. The main part of the circle is easily set out on the ground using equilateral triangles, two radial edges of which are then bisected to find the centres of the shorter arcs. The longer arc then follows automatically.

This type A flattened circle has fixed proportions and is thus always the same shape, or geometrically similar, no matter what scale it is drawn at. It has a ratio between its circumference and the major diameter of 3.059 and may represent an early attempt by Neolithic man to rationalize what we call pi (π) . Quite remarkably Lawford appears to have been set out using this shape as a template, the basic circular section having a radius of 13 of Thom's Megalithic Yards of 2.72 feet (829mm).

Thom's use of a blend of Geometry, Astronomy and Statistics to prove his results may have led the archaeologists astray. Whilst they too were increasingly using modern scientific methods in their work, they interpreted his work as implying that Neolithic man had these same skills.

Taking a step backwards and relying more on intuition is perhaps helpful here; the question we need to ask at this point is whether the symmetry we are observing is real or imagined. Although parts of the flattened circle appear to have been lost there is sufficient remaining, especially in the form of the two shoulders, for any intelligent being to read the pattern. This is even more the case for the site at Flixton and can only indicate a deliberate intention on the builders' part to erect a flattened circle. To imagine that they were mere primitives and that what we see are misshapen attempts to set out a true circle is facile.

This is the more so when at both Lawford and Flixton the axis of symmetry created by the flattening of the circle provides an accurate alignment to the rising or setting of the moon at its maximum northwards declination. Whilst the cycle of the sun's motion is easily observed by reference to its rising or setting point on the horizon, having a maximum bearing northwards at midsummer and southwards at midwinter, the moon presents the next natural challenge. Its motions are more complex, but the connection between its monthly phases and the tides would not have been missed by the Neolithic's early seafarers. Observation by the same method relative to the horizon would be easy, but would take a little longer to reveal the moon's 18.6 year cycle of maxima and minima.

SUMMARY

In conclusion then, we seem to have a set of post-holes at Lawford whose plan geometry appears to match that of many stone circles, using the same unit of measurement as proposed by Thom. Its geometrical symmetry identifies an axis to the north-east where the moon rises at its maximum northwards declination. The circle also seems to have been sited so that this axis lies over a tributary valley to the north-east, providing a topographical sight line in that direction, where the moon at its maximum would appear to have grazed up the side of the valley, before appearing above the horizon.

Basically the evidence at Lawford is as good as at many a stone circle, and it is perhaps to be regretted that it was not better recorded or investigated, particularly with respect to what it could offer in terms of astronomical potential. Unfortunately now we only have a paper memory of the monument's former existence, a reminder for the future that we need to better appreciate what our ancestors were capable of, in order to begin finding the right evidence.

REFERENCES

Gibson, A. 1998 *Stonehenge & Timber Circles* Tempus

Heath, R. 2007 *Alexander Thom: Cracking the Stone Age Code*
Bluestone Press

Shennan, S.J., Healy, F. & Smith, I.F. 1985 *The Excavation of a Ring-Ditch at Tye Field, Lawford, Essex*
Archaeological Journal vol.142, pp.150-215

Taylor, P. 2010 *Lawford: A Timber Circle Overlooked* Polystar Press

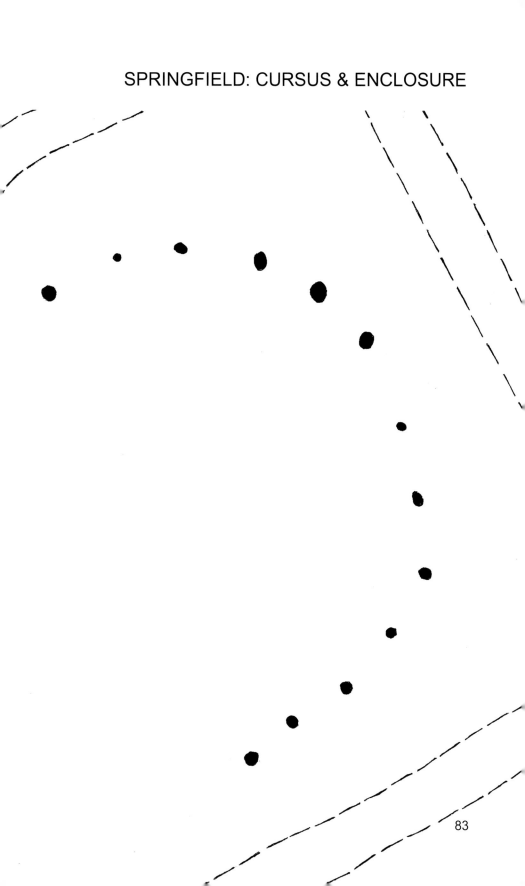

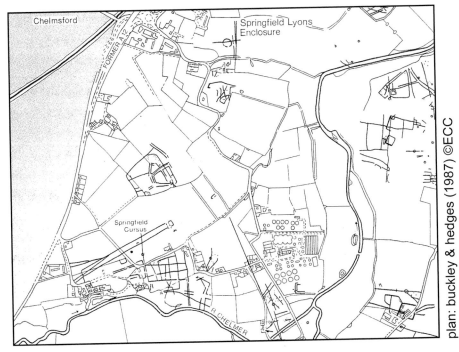

plan: buckley & hedges (1987) ©ECC

As the Arminghall henge is to Norwich, so the Springfield site is to Chelmsford, another riverside monument but this time in southern Essex. About two miles east of the town, between the old A12 through and the new by-pass around, a site being dug prior to the development of 'Chelmer Village' yielded amongst other things a sizeable cursus monument some 700 metres in length and 40 metres wide.

The cursus was aligned roughly south-west to north-east, parallel to the general direction of the river valley thereabouts and had enclosed within its eastern end at TL 732071 the remains of a circular setting of timber posts. Remains they are because the thirteen post-holes still extant formed only a semi-circle, truncated to the south-west by drainage works cutting across the cursus that had eradicated all trace of the other posts before the dig took place.

So as with the other timber circles we have seen, the evidence here is limited, but not so as to tell us nothing. Although there is some irregularity and flattening around the semi-circle of posts, our eyes still tell us this was in all probability originally a circular setting of timbers, perhaps now with some ten posts missing.

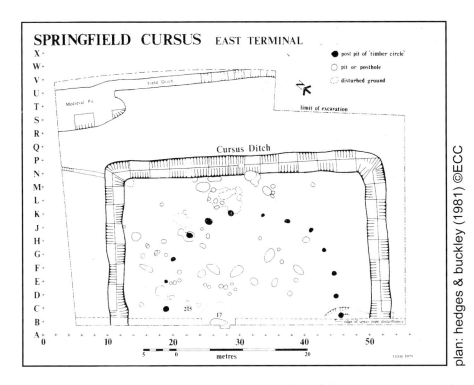

SPRINGFIELD CURSUS EAST TERMINAL

● post pit of 'timber circle'
○ pit or posthole
⬭ disturbed ground

limit of excavation

Cursus Ditch

Field Ditch

Medieval Pit

plan: hedges & buckley (1981) ©ECC

The setting sits very centrally within the outline of the cursus, apparently equidistant from both the sides and the eastern terminus. A reflected overlay applied here will do little but confirm this and bring to light the other outstanding feature here: the central axis of the cursus itself.

Looking in more detail, the circle of posts fits well with a circle of diameter 32 Megalithic Yards, which seems the more right when we find the ditches of the cursus spaced apart some 48 MY, half as much again. The axis here on a monument some 700 metres long is not to be ignored lightly, but its orientation seems strange at first - certainly not towards any of the solar or lunar maxima with which we have become accustomed at these sites.

With the low lying terrain here, there are not any significant landscape pointers in any other directions, so we have to deal with what we have in the form of an axis with amplitude 28° from grid, 26° from true east-west. Using Thom's table with the necessary corrections for latitude and altitude we find the alignment represents the rising or setting point of an object with declination around 16°. This is surprisingly close to the right amount to be indicative of the sun on what we now call the cross quarter days.

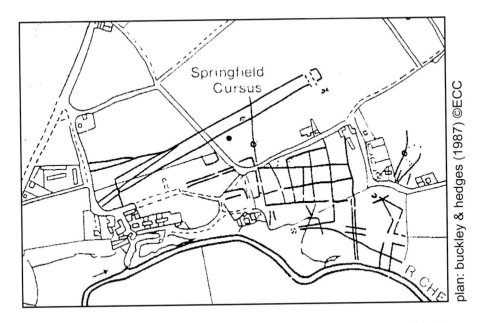

Springfield
Cursus

plan: buckley & hedges (1987) ©ECC

As I write this in early February, it is indeed one of those cross quarter days and the sun would be setting along the line of the cursus to the west-south-west, having last done so some three months previously in early November last year. In the meantime it will have consistently set further south reaching its maximum southwards declination at the winter solstice.

Moving into the spring, the sun will rise and set gradually further northwards each day, with a true east-west transit being observed on the equinox itself. Looking ahead to early May, we can see that turning the alignment through 180°, it will then be possible to mark out when the sun rises along the line of the cursus to the east-north-east. This provides another quarter day marker, prior to the sun's maximum northwards declination being reached at the summer solstice, this period being closed by the other quarter day in early August when the sun again rises along the same line.

We seem to have invented a calendar here, the alignment along the cursus allowing the subdivision of the year into four more or less equal seasons. Each quarter day would be followed a month and a half later (approx. 46 days) by either solstice or equinox, any sums necessary, here perhaps aided by the circle itself with its 23 posts? The cross quarter days in their christianised form are Candlemas, Mayday, Lammas and All Hallows, but they go back further than that and were the basis of the Celtic calendar known as Imbolc, Beltane, Lughnasa and Samhain, falling at the beginning of February, May, August and November respectively.

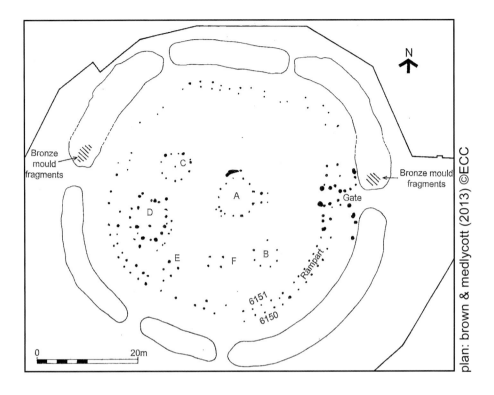

About 1200 metres to the north of the cursus site, higher on the valley side a large circular monument known as the Springfield Lyons enclosure was excavated in the 1980's.

Not dissimilar to many other sites of this nature, it comprised a large circular ditch some 60 metres in diameter, originally in six segments, with six possible entrances. It contained at least four circular settings of timber posts up to 10 metres in diameter, the remains of round-houses, the whole lot of Late Bronze Age date rather than timber circles of Neolithic date.

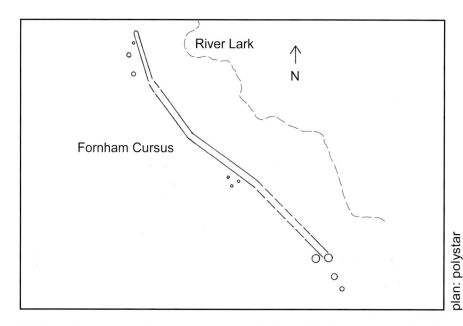

River Lark

N

Fornham Cursus

plan: polystar

Whilst writing about this one cursus at Springfield, this might be the best place to mention the presence of others in the East Anglian landscape, particularly in Suffolk. Like most of our timber circles, they do in general lie within river valleys and are often associated with larger assemblages of Neolithic remains.

We will see more in the section concerning the Fenland timber circles, but should note at this point the presence of a quite large cursus, some 1800 metres long by 35 metres wide, at Fornham All Saints in the valley of the River Lark near Bury St Edmunds in west Suffolk. This one runs roughly north-west to south-east, but meanders a little having four main sections with three slight bends between them. It does not seem to be associated with a particular timber circle, although any one of several circular crop-marks at the south-eastern end may prove to be such.

Again as I write, now later in February, it has come to light that the Fornham Cursus is soon to be excavated, so in due course we might well have another eastern timber circle to add to our collection, but probably not before this is published later this year (2015). Two further simpler and smaller cursuses, more akin to the Springfield example, are to be found in south Suffolk on the north side of the River Stour. One is south of Sudbury near Bures St Mary, the other much further downstream towards the Lawford timber circle, at Stratford St Mary.

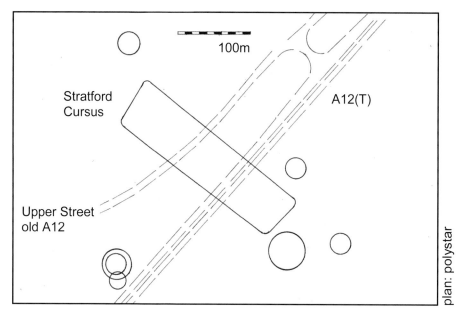

On the south Suffolk border at TM 048344 the Stratford St Mary cursus sits astride the A12(T) by-pass, basically aligned north-west to south-east. Like the Fornham example it also has several perhaps promising ring-ditch sites near its south-eastern terminus, another to the north and a single and a double ring-ditch a short distance away to the south-west. There is also nearby to the east the cropmark outline of a long barrow.

I would put money on at least one of these ring-ditches concealing a timber circle. This site lies within the valley of the River Stour not only near many ring-ditches, but away on a nearby hill-top to the north-north-east there is a site shown on the OS map as a henge monument, perhaps mistakenly as in later times it was used as a windmill mount.

The cursus as plotted on the OS map from aerial photographs is some 290 metres long and 60 metres wide and has a very clear orientation 38.5° north of grid west. This represents an amplitude from true west of 40.9°. Allowing for a latitude of 51.97° and altitude of 0.95°, adjusted downwards for refraction to 0.50°, we get from Thom's table a declination for a body setting to the north-west of 24.15°.

This is only 0.23°, just less than half the width of the suns' disc, more than the sun's maximum declination in Neolithic times of 23.92°. The alignment thus points rather accurately towards the upper limb or last setting point of the sun.

REFERENCES

Brown, N. & Medlycott, M. 2013 *The Neolithic and Bronze Age Enclosures at Springfield Lyons, Essex: Excavations 1981-1991* East Anglian Archaeology 149

Buckley, D & Hedges, J. 1987 *The Bronze Age and Saxon Settlements at Springfield Lyons, Essex, an interim report* Essex CC occ. paper 5

Buckley, D., Hedges, J. & Brown, N. 2001 *Excavations at a Neolithic Cursus, Springfield, Essex 1979-85* Proceedings of the Prehistoric Society vol.67 pp.101-162 Cambridge UP

Dymond, D. & Martin, E. (eds) 1999 *An Historical Atlas of Suffolk* Suffolk CC / SIAH

Gibson, A. 1998 *Stonehenge & Timber Circles* Tempus

Hedges, J. & Buckley, D. 1981 *Springfield Cursus and the Cursus problem* Essex CC occ. paper 1

Hutton, R. 1996 *The Stations of the Sun* Oxford UP

Loveday, R. 2006 *Inscribed across the Landscape: The Cursus Enigma* Tempus

Martin, E.A. 1982 *When is a Henge not a Henge?* Proceedings of Suffolk Institute of Archaeology and History XXXV part 2, pp.141-143

North, J. 1996 *Stonehenge: Neolithic Man and the Cosmos* HarperCollins

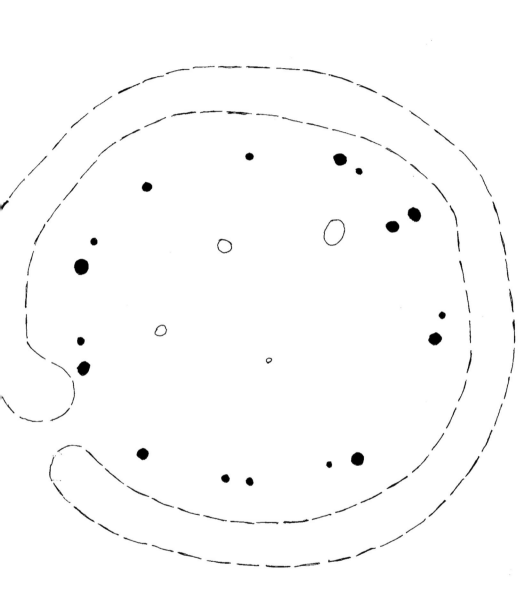

INTRODUCTION

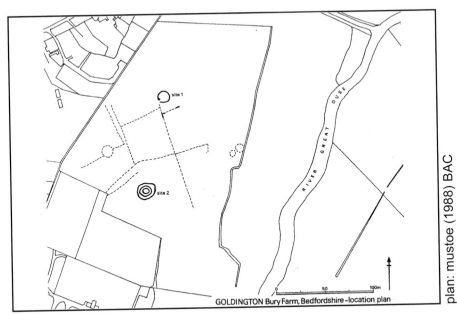

plan: mustoe (1988) BAC

GOLDINGTON Bury Farm, Bedfordshire - location plan

In the late 1980's a rescue archaeology dig was undertaken in the village of Goldington, about two miles east of Bedford town centre. A superstore and housing development were to be built, coincidentally designed by the local architectural practice of Woods Hardwick, for whom the author had briefly worked from 1981 to 1983.

The dig focused on a number of 'ring ditches', those mysterious circular monuments usually identified by aerial photography, which usually ended up classified as the remains of Bronze Age burials. At TL 079505, one of these turned out to be a circular ditch, in fact a Neolithic henge monument that had lost its bank and within which were found a number of post-holes: a 'timber circle' as we now know it.

About 200 metres to the south-south-west (TL 078503) a second slightly larger monument was found comprising three near-circular ditches with a few post-holes on the northern side between the middle and outer ditches. The centre of this had been mounded over and used for Bronze Age burials at a later date.

Fig.1 of the archaeologist's 'preliminary report' showing the whole site and local area is reproduced above, but it should be noted that the scale bar is incorrectly shown as 100 metres long, whereas in reality it should be 200 metres - presumably a result of over-hasty publication.

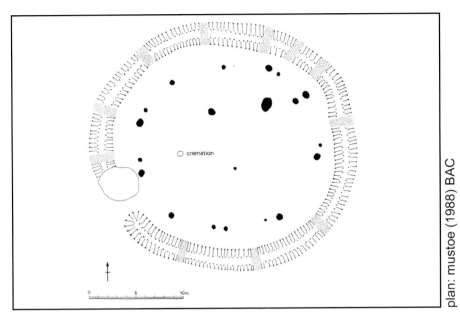

plan: mustoe (1988) BAC

On closer inspection the 'circle' of timbers is actually more elliptical in plan and has the unusual feature of most of the timber posts being paired, comprising three single posts and seven pairs, seventeen in total. The layout is such that each post or pair has a gap between posts or pairs diametrically opposite it, mainly caused by the gap on the south-east side being about a 'gap and a half' compared to the rest. The paired posts all seem to be a standard distance of about 1½ metres apart, with six of the pairs spaced around the circumference.

The remaining pair of posts notably has the posts spaced radially and is on the north-east side, a position more or less opposite the presumed 'entrance' to the monument indicated by a gap in the ditch on the south-west side. The archaeologists note that the ditch had been recut a number of times, indicating a lengthy period of use for the monument. Three further holes and the site of a Bronze Age cremation are indicated in the central space on the archaeologist's plan, as above, although the report refers to two cremations and does not make anything of what the holes might have been for.

This is surprising considering the essential symmetry that presents itself here in the plan, almost as if the archaeologists did not want to find anything indicative of an intelligence capable of accurately setting out such a near-circular shape. Their mistaken presumption seems to have been that it was not a true circle because Neolithic man was not even capable of setting out something as simple as a circle.

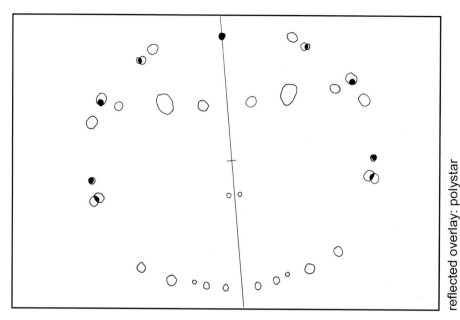

reflected overlay: polystar

Using the human eye and brain to find the best fit with a reflected overlay of the plan works well here, with several post positions duplicating either side of a very nearly north-south axis and a single axial post on the northern side.

Looking at the archaeologist's site layout plan relative to a modern OS map, it can be deduced that the north point given, parallel to the sides of the illustration, is in fact grid north, true north for this site being some 1.25° west of this. The same must be assumed for the plan given for the circle, so that this axis found is some 4.9° west of grid and therefore 3.65° west of true north.

Had Neolithic man bisected horizon positions of the rising and setting sun to establish a north-south line, it would have deviated only 0.1° west of north at midsummer and 0.2° east of north (the wrong way) at midwinter. The latter is because the south eastern horizon over a low ridge of hills some four miles distant has an altitude about five times higher than the low river valley horizon to the south-west. The 3.65° skew of the monument's axis away from true north-south must therefore be either deliberate or totally accidental - we may never know which or why.

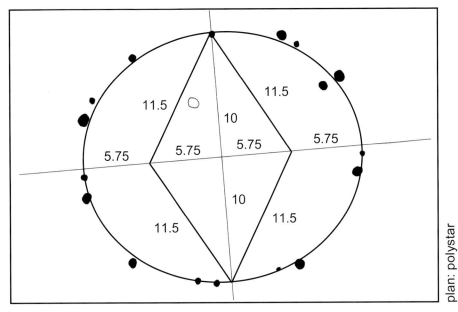

plan: polystar

Using this axis and its perpendicular cross axis for setting out purposes, diameters of 20 and 23 Megalithic Yards can be seen to fit fairly well with the plan form.

An ellipse conforming to these dimensions can be formed by simply dissecting the major axis twice, creating a very near right-angled triangle of sides 5.75, 10 and 11.5 MY (to be absolutely correct this triangle would have angles 30°, 60° and 90° and the 10 would actually be 9.96). Such an ellipse is probably the easiest of all to set out and has a value of circumference to major diameter, π' = 2.940, not dissimilar to the value for a type B flattened circle. Plotted this way, the ellipse can be seen to be a little short of the posts away from the cardinal directions.

An alternative setting out for this monument is therefore suggested as shown overleaf, comprising two semicircles of radius 10 MY set some 3 MY apart. This certainly fits better at the 'corners' and interestingly comes up with a much improved value for π' of 2.993.

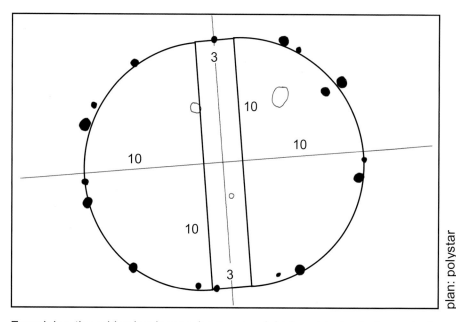

plan: polystar

Examining the wider landscape here, we might be able to deduce whether there are any astronomical reasons the circle is the way it is. Basically the site sits at about 25m above OD in the wide flood plain of the River Great Ouse with no immediately obvious landscape features nearby.

The river runs roughly south-west to north-east as does a ridge of limestone about four miles to the south-east that is 90m above OD south of the site, running down to only 30m in the east. The opposite north-western bank of the river is more convoluted and cut by valleys, having an average height of 70m above OD about three miles from the river.

The horizon is thus elevated some 40m, 6000m away to the south-east, 25m, 3000m away to the north-east, 55m, 5000m to the north-west and only 5m, 4000m up the river valley to the south-west. This means that the altitudes in these directions are 0.38°, 0.48°, 0.63° and 0.07° respectively.

Using a latitude of 52.15° and feeding these altitudes into Thom's table we can find the amplitudes (angles from due east-west) for the extreme rising and setting points of the sun and moon.

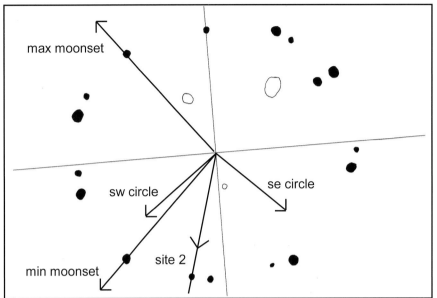

plan: polystar

Plotting these values back onto our plans we find the midwinter sun lines both pass through circular but unidentified features shown on the site plan to the south-east and south-west. This may not have been the case when the timber circle was first built, as these features are most likely to be 'ring ditches', the remains of Bronze Age burial mounds, deliberately built later at these significant positions relative to the circle.

In addition the two extreme moonset positions in the west appear to be identified from the centre of the circle by the two western single post positions, the only single posts other than the axial northern one. The declinations indicated by the centre lines of these posts when viewed from the centre of the circle are both around 27.5°, but any accurate reading of the moon's position would have to be made using a foresight at a greater distance.

In the absence of any notable landscape features, there would have to have been distant posts positioned at a suitable distance to pin down accurately the moon's position. We are unlikely to find these now, so was all this by accident or by design?

Also from the centre of the circle, the westernmost of the two southern posts interestingly points towards the second site to the south-south-west, some 190 metres distant (230 MY).

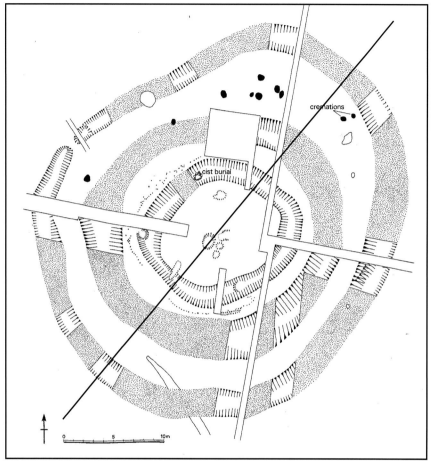

plan: mustoe (1988) BAC

This second site mainly comprises three concentric ditches, the inner two nearly circular, the outer one somewhat egg-shaped with the sharp end pointing to the north-east. The egg seems more like one of Thom's type I on the south-east side, but more like type II on the north-west, where there is a straighter section on the outer ditch. It was described by the archaeologists as a triple ring burial mound, but seems to have been ditches at first with burials and a central mound covering where the inner ditch was added later.

Applying a reflected overlay to this plan, an axis emerges to the north-east some 49° north of grid, i.e. 47.75° north of true east. Using Thom's table, this amplitude with the requisite adjustments for latitude, altitude and parallax corresponds with a declination of 28.07°, pretty much the northernmost rising point of the moon.

Gibson, A. 1998 *Stonehenge & Timber Circles* Tempus

Heath, R. 2007 *Alexander Thom: Cracking the Stone Age Code*
Bluestone Press

Mustoe, R.S. 1988 *Salvage Excavation of a Neolithic and Bronze Age Ritual Site at Goldington, Bedford: A Preliminary Report*
Bedfordshire Archaeology vol.18 pp.1-5

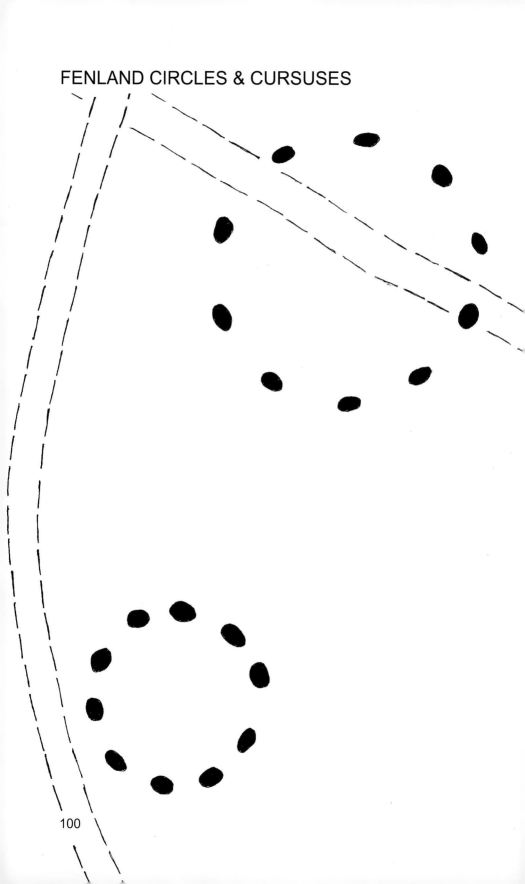

100

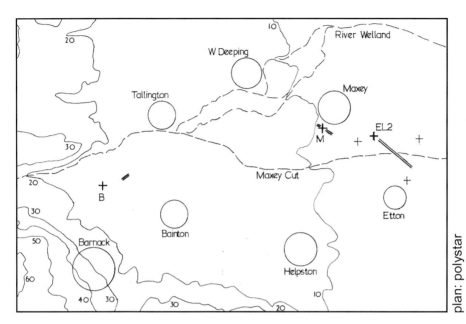

plan: polystar

We have thus far examined the evidence for timber circles in the counties of Norfolk, Suffolk, Essex and Bedfordshire and must now conclude our tour of the eastern counties in Cambridgeshire. Three sites are known from archaeological digs in the Fens, all essentially just inside the county boundary along the southern side of the River Welland: Barnack, Maxey and Etton. They are by now for the most part lost to gravel workings within the floodplain, so once again we are dealing with paper heritage.

A fourth site given by Gibson (1998) lies a little to the north at Deeping St Nicholas in Lincolnshire, but this is basically a Bronze Age burial site used several times, each time usually involving the construction or reconstruction of an earth mound retained by timber posts or stake-settings, not quite a proper timber circle, but then nor is the one at Holme typical.

All three sites that follow here have associated cursuses and it seems these become more prevalent the flatter the landscape. Without a variable horizon there to provide features against which the rising or setting of the sun or moon can be assessed, it must have become necessary to insert a feature into the landscape with a strong directional emphasis.

The circles of pits, some with posts, are also different here, being mainly circular in shape; presumably with the cursuses providing directional orientation, the circles did not need to. It will be recalled that the already discussed site at Springfield had the same characteristics.

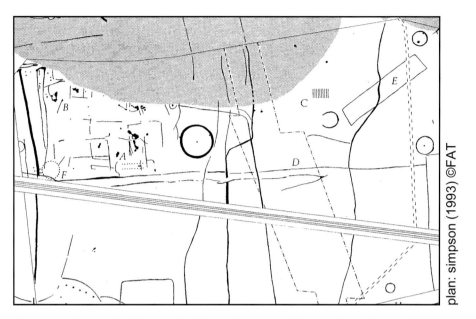

plan: simpson (1993) ©FAT

About a mile north of Barnack village, there are the remains of some 24 pits set in circle situated just north of the Peterborough to Stamford railway line (TF 079066). Just where the River Welland emerges from the adjoining limestone hills, it is at the western edge of an extensive area investigated for its numerous cropmarks by the Welland Valley Project from 1981.

Further east within the project area there are many other circular features including a large ring-ditch similar in size to an early Bronze Age example that was excavated at Tallington about a mile and a half to the north-east. There is also an approximately 20 metres by 110 metres Neolithic cursus type monument at TF 083067 with a north-east to south-west alignment.

Unfortunately none of these seem to have been excavated as yet, or if they have the results have not been published. All we have thus far is a paper with a general overview of the site as above that deals mainly with the excavation of later Romano-British aisled buildings.

From the overall plan of the site shown above, assuming it is set parallel to grid north, we can at least have a stab at assessing in which direction the cursus itself is aligned. Taken as 36.0° from grid east-west, we get 34.73° from true east-west, this value being taken as our amplitude. Assuming a horizon to the north-east at zero altitude, we need to use an altitude value of -0.47° to allow for atmospheric refraction.

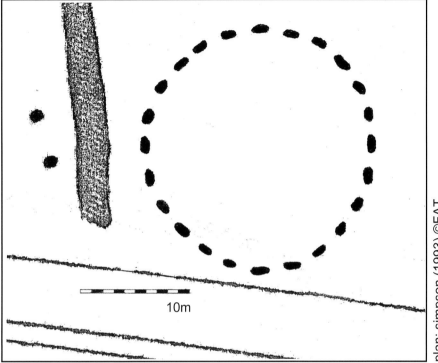

plan: simpson (1993) ©FAT

Putting these values plus a latitude of 52.65° into Thom's table we arrive at a declination for any body rising along the line of the cursus to the north-east of 19.83°. This is perhaps unremarkable and certainly not a quarter day value such as might help keep a calendar as we saw at Springfield.

However it is near the moon's maximum northwards declination at minor standstill, something not directly observable as an extreme on the horizon. It is rather a minimum maximum, which would have been logged amongst a long run of observations.

As for the circle, all we can do is attempt a simple enlargement to a scale comparable to our other circles. The quality is not good, but sufficient to see that this is not quite a perfect circle and not a draughtsman's approximation to such, in which case there would be a series of dotted lines rather than the apparent variable post-holes of slightly differing profile that are shown.

All we have to go on is its description as a pit-circle (not necessarily with posts) some 21 metres in diameter, a touch larger than those found further east at Maxey of 10 and 15 metres diameter (qv).

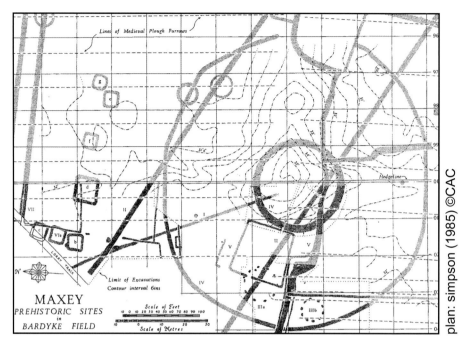

Lines of Medieval Plough Furrows

Hedgeline

Limit of Excavations
Contour interval 6ins

MAXEY
PREHISTORIC SITES
in
BARDYKE FIELD

Scale of Feet
10 0 10 20 30 40 50 60 70 80 90 100

Scale of Metres
0 10 20 30

plan: simpson (1985) ©CAC

About three miles east of the Barnack site, another at Maxey was discovered by aerial photography just after World War II and excavated in the 1960's when there was a threat from proposed gravel extraction works. It proved equally complex with many different layers of cropmarks and enclosures to unravel. Amongst them are two pit-circles, each of ten holes and both situated to the west of a 40 metre diameter ring-ditch. All three of these lie within an outer concentric ring-ditch some 120 metres in diameter.

The larger northern circle and the inner ring-ditch at approximately TF 125077 are both traversed by the southern ditch of a large cursus set on a north-west to south-east alignment. The second ditch of this cursus is some 58 metres further to the north-east, passing just within the outer ring-ditch but with its termini remaining well outside the area drawn.

From the overall plan of the site shown above, assuming its north point arrow is set parallel to grid north, we can try to determine in which direction this cursus is aligned. It is 31.50° from grid east-west which is thus 32.83° from true east-west, this value being taken as our amplitude. Assuming a horizon 20 metres high some 8,000 metres to the north-west we have an altitude value of 0.14° which has to be adjusted downwards to -0.33° to allow for refraction by the atmosphere.

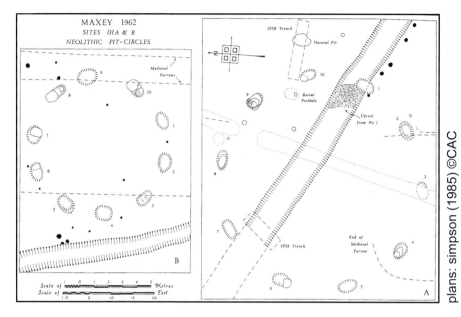

plans: simpson (1985) ©CAC

Putting these values plus a latitude of 52.65° into Thom's table we arrive at a declination of for any body rising along the line of this cursus of 18.92°. Like the Barnack example, this could well represent the moon's minimum maximum at minor standstill.

The pit-circles (shown on section frontispiece at 1:200) are centred about 25 metres apart, and are reportedly 15 and 10 metres in diameter. These particular values equate well with dimensions measured in Megalithic Yards of 30, 18 and 12, whilst the separation of the two cursus ditches at 58 metres equates to 70 MY. Similarly the radii of the two ring-ditches equate to 24 and 72 MY.

It is quite possible we do not have a real timber circle here as the pits are thought too shallow to have held posts, but at least they contained various Neolithic sherds confirming their date. They appeared to have been redug at some point and a lack of weathering to the sides suggested to the archaeologists they had been refilled soon after being dug.

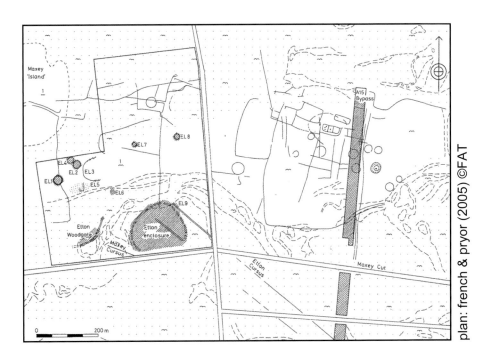

plan: french & pryor (2005) ©FAT

About a mile further east from the Maxey site there is a third complex in this small but interesting area at Etton, just north of Maxey Cut that here by-passes the River Welland to the south. Here there is the eastern end of the Maxey cursus just described, and a section of another, the Etton cursus.

The latter runs north-west to south-east and has an amplitude of 39.5° from grid east-west, 40.83° from true east-west. Using the same values for latitude and altitude as the nearby Maxey example, we can deduce that this new amplitude represents a declination for a body setting to the north-west of some 23.07°. It seems we have another pointer to midsummer sunset here as we did at Stratford St Mary in Suffolk.

Three sites within the complex, Etton Landscape numbers 2, 4 and 7 at the north-west end of the cursus, are identified as henges. Fairly close together, they occupy a slightly higher area of the terraced river gravels. Site EL7 is a very simple classic henge containing but one pit and site EL4 to its west has a small off-centre setting of pits. However site EL2 at TF 136076 is the most interesting as it lies south-east of and immediately adjacent to the site EL4 henge and comprises a circular ditch containing a setting of seven posts, one on its own plus three in a line due east-west and three in a line pointing east-north-east to west-south-west, possibly another minimum maximum moon direction.

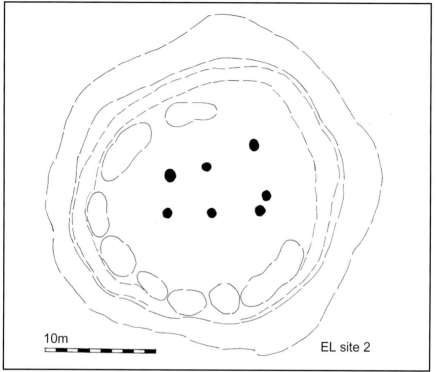

10m

EL site 2

plan: polystar

The post-holes and ditch of EL2 have been identified as the earliest phase of several as three further ditches were later dug: one inside more tightly containing the post-holes (not shown above) and then one more just inside (but only horseshoe shaped and open to the north-east rather like Stonehenge's trilithons) and one just outside the original ditch, their discovery and unraveling all to the credit of the archaeologist's skills.

Further west at TF 132075 a triple ring-ditch, excavated in 1977 by Robert Powell, also showed promise, but this seems more likely to have been a probably later palisade type monument. A series of closely spaced post-holes had been dug into the bottom of the inner of three concentric ditches about 20 metres in diameter.

Two further sites have been identified by aerial photography that might prove to be henges with settings of pits or posts. They are both north-east of Etton village at TF 143067, just south of South Drain and TF 146076, just east of the A15 by-pass road outside the area excavated there.

REFERENCES

French, C. 1991 *Excavation of Deeping St. Nicholas Barrow Site 28,
Lincolnshire* Antiquity 65 pp.580-582

French, C. & Pryor, F. 2005 *Archaeology and Environment of the Etton
Landscape* East Anglian Archaeology 109

Gibson, A. 1998 *Stonehenge & Timber Circles* Tempus

Loveday, R. 2006 *Inscribed across the Landscape: The Cursus Enigma*
Tempus

Powell, R. 1977 *A Triple Ring-Ditch at Maxey* Durobrivae 5

Simpson, W.G. 1985 *Excavations at Maxey, Bardyke Field, 1962-63*
East Anglian Archaeology 27 vol.2 pp.245-264

Simpson, W.G. 1993 *The Excavation of Romano-British Aisled Buildings at
Barnack, Cambridgeshire* East Anglian Archaeology 61 pp.102-126

IN CONCLUSION

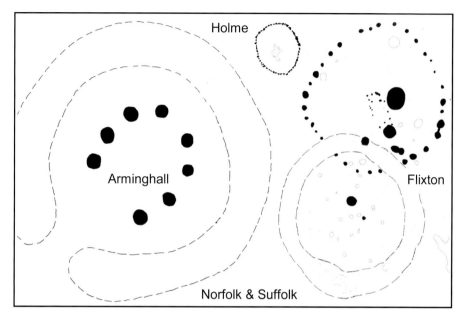

The story of the discovery of the timber circles is itself instructive in charting the history of archaeology from its early days as a humanity subject to now when it has become more of a scientific enquiry. The early digs such as at Arminghall dealt with what was at the time purely a curiosity, a henge monument with timbers instead of stone, discovered by the then new technique of aerial photography. It seems to have been excavated as if it were a stone monument for which the stones would have remained forever to take their story into the future.

Fortunately, unlike many more recent digs, this site is a Scheduled Monument and does remain available to us and presumably the holes dug were carefully backfilled. Thus a new dig could well find much the same, apart from the Neolithic fills that have gone, and provide us with the missing orientation so poorly recorded by the use of a magnetic north taken below high voltage power lines! Nearby the Markshall site, also a Scheduled Monument, remains undug and at threat from eradication by the plough.

Later digs such as at Lawford in 1962/3 seem to have been under-resourced as only half the site was dug at that time, a couple of years after the site had also been picked up by aerial photography. Again the north point was a little questionable, as it did not line up with the presumed grid north used for the second half of the site in 1971. The paper summarising these results did not appear until 1985 and did not even attempt to stitch the two halves of the site together to produce a unified plan.

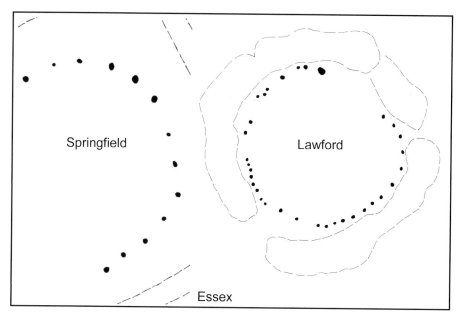

The site at Maxey was also excavated in 1962/3 and similarly waited until 1985 for publication. It too has a slightly indeterminate north point a little out from a strange grid of northings and westings used to locate various parts of the site. Nowadays everything is at least plotted up relative to the national grid with its eastings and northings, so that by 1997 when Flixton came along, there was little dispute about how the site was actually set in the wider landscape.

I say 'was' because by then we were in the era of 'rescue archaeology', a misnomer if ever there was. The sites at Springfield (1980) and Goldington (1988) were both rapidly dug to extract as much information from the ground as could be achieved at the time, prior to redevelopment. All we have now for these is the paper record, which was produced at the time without a clue that there might be such a thing as a 'timber circle' type of monument or that alignments to a distant horizon might be significant.

As we have already noted very few of our timber circles are actually circular in plan and for comparison they are all shown above and adjoining at a scale of approximately 1:500. Even Flixton first appeared as a 'sub-circular enclosure' until it was spotted by the present author in an annual Archaeological Service report, providing the impetus that eventually led to the production of the present volume.

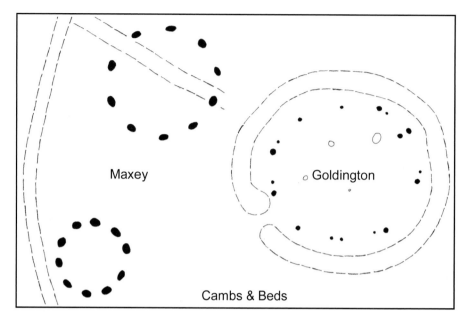

Maxey

Goldington

Cambs & Beds

The appearance of Gibson's 'Stonehenge & Timber Circles' soon after remedied all this with a new category of monument, recognised mainly as precursors to stone monuments in the west, but still a curiosity over here in the east.

Firmly in the archaeological camp, Gibson had little time for archaeoastronomers' and mathematicians' ideas about orientations at megalithic sites, stating '*Furthermore if these sites were complex calendars and observatories then they suggest a level of numeracy amongst the prehistoric population far in excess of that which has hitherto been imagined...*' Indeed they do and so too its seems do the timber examples.

He does accept the possibility of establishing the cardinal points, but supposes this can be done by observing the midday winter sun, but how do you know it is midday other than by observing that the sun is due south? This circular argument exposes a lack of understanding in the archaeological world tempered it seems by a desire not to understand.

Part of the problem with the archaeological world accepting Thom's work must be related to its timing, coming as it did on the heels of the radiocarbon revolution, which had forced the archaeologists to reluctantly recalibrate their time scales. The implications of both on the accepted ideas of gentle diffusion of civilisation from the east to the west were enormous and difficult to assimilate.

painting: dil andrews

I am sure the archaeologists still find the geometry and astronomy a challenge, but they do now at least employ quite complex scientific analysis as part of their remit in particular with the minutiae of a dig looking at beetle wing-cases, plant seeds and even pollen grains, in addition to the now commonplace search for a piece of unadulterated carbon-based matter for radio-carbon dating.

With the geometry and astronomy we may never know the whole story, but this book has attempted to pull together further evidence from the eastern counties to show that Thom's theories can sensibly be applied here too. Whether he was right or whether his theories could equally well be applied to a set of car park bollards in Sudbury will be a matter of personal judgement as nothing can be categorically proven.

I tend to rely on my intuition, which is telling me that Neolithic man was indeed brighter than he has been given credit for, which leads me to the opinion that Thom was right. The plan forms are not accidentally misshapen attempts at circles and the alignments, particularly those towards the moon's extreme positions, are far from accidental. With so many sites with potential solar and lunar alignments here in the east perhaps as yet undiscovered, the important thing is to record what is found fully and accurately, keeping an open mind that allows for any new shred of evidence or line of enquiry to at least have its voice heard and be considered.

COLLECTED REFERENCES

Ashwin, T. 2000 *Excavations at Harford Farm, Caistor St Edmund, 1990*
              East Anglian Archaeology 91
Ashwin, T. & Davison, A. 2005 *An Historical Atlas of Norfolk* Phillimore
Beex, W. & Peterson, J. 2004 *The Arminghall Henge in Space and Time*
              BAR International 1227
Boulter, S. 1998 *Flixton Park, Flixton*
              Suffolk CC Archaeological Report 97/53
Boulter, S. & Walton Rogers, P. 2012 *Circles and Cemeteries: Excavations
              at Flixton Volume 1* East Anglian Archaeology 147
Bradley, R. 1997 *Rock Art and the Prehistory of Atlantic Europe* Routledge
Brennand, M. & Taylor, M. 2003 *The Survey and Excavation of a Bronze
    Age Timber Circle at Holme-next-the-Sea, Norfolk 1998-9*
    Proceedings of the Prehistoric Society vol.69 pp.1-84 Cambridge UP
Brown, N. & Medlycott, M. 2013 *The Neolithic and Bronze Age Enclosures
              at Springfield Lyons, Essex: Excavations 1981-1991*
              East Anglian Archaeology 149
Buckley, D & Hedges, J. 1987 *The Bronze Age and Saxon Settlements at
    Springfield Lyons, Essex, an interim report*   Essex CC occ. paper 5
Buckley, D., Hedges, J. & Brown, N. 2001 *Excavations at a Neolithic Cursus,
              Springfield, Essex 1979-85* Proceedings of the
              Prehistoric Society vol.67 pp.101-162 Cambridge UP
Burl, A. 1976 *The Stone Circles of the British Isles* Yale UP
Clark, G. 1936 *The Timber Monument at Arminghall and its Affinities*
          Proceedings of the Prehistoric Society vol.2 pp.1-51 Cambridge UP
Critchlow, K. 1969 *Order in Space* Thames & Hudson
Critchlow, K. 2007 *Time Stands Still* Floris Books
Dymond, D. & Martin, E. (eds) 1999 *An Historical Atlas of Suffolk* SIAH
French, C. 1991 *Excavation of Deeping St. Nicholas Barrow Site 28,
              Lincolnshire* Antiquity 65 pp.580-582
French, C. & Pryor, F. 2005 *Archaeology and Environment of the Etton
              Landscape* East Anglian Archaeology 109
Gibson, A. 1998 *Stonehenge & Timber Circles* Tempus
Harding, J. 2003 *Henge Monuments of the British Isles* Tempus
Heath, R. 2007 *Alexander Thom: Cracking the Stone Age Code* Bluestone
Hedges, J. & Buckley, D. 1981 *Springfield Cursus and the Cursus problem*
              Essex CC occ. paper 1
Hutton, R. 1996 *The Stations of the Sun* Oxford UP
Loveday, R. 2006 *Inscribed across the Landscape: The Cursus Enigma*
              Tempus
Marshall, D.N. 1977 *Carved Stone Balls* Proc Soc Antiq Scot 108 pp.4-72
Marshall, D.N. 1983 *Further Notes on Carved Stone Balls*
              Proc Soc Antiq Scot 113 pp.628-646
Martin, E.A. 1982 *When is a Henge not a Henge?* Proceedings of Suffolk
          Institute of Archaeology and History XXXV part 2, pp.141-143

Morris, R.W.B. 1977 *Prehistoric Rock Art of Argyll* Dolphin
Morris, R.W.B. 1979 *Prehistoric Rock Art of Galloway and the Isle of Man* Blandford
Mustoe, R.S. 1988 *Salvage Excavation of a Neolithic and Bronze Age Ritual Site at Goldington, Bedford: A Preliminary Report* Bedfordshire Archaeology vol.18 pp.1-5
North, J. 1996 *Stonehenge: Neolithic Man and the Cosmos* HarperCollins
Parker Pearson, M. 2012 *Stonehenge* Simon & Schuster
Pitts, M. 2000 *Hengeworld* Arrow
Powell, R. 1977 *A Triple Ring-Ditch at Maxey* Durobrivae 5
Pryor, F. 2001 *Seahenge* Harper Collins
Ruggles, C.L.N. (ed) 1988 *Records in Stone Papers in Memory of Alexander Thom* Cambridge UP
Ruggles, C. 1999 *Astronomy in Prehistoric Britain and Ireland* Yale UP
Ruggles, C. 2006 *Astronomical Potential of the Flixton Timber Circle* Report for Suffolk CC
Shennan, S.J., Healy, F. & Smith, I.F. 1985 *The Excavation of a Ring-Ditch at Tye Field, Lawford, Essex* Archaeological Journal vol.142, pp.150-215
Simpson, W.G. 1985 *Excavations at Maxey, Bardyke Field, 1962-63* East Anglian Archaeology 27 vol.2 pp.245-264
Simpson, W.G. 1993 *The Excavation of Romano-British Aisled Buildings at Barnack, Cambridgeshire* East Anglian Archaeology 61 pp.102-126
Taylor, P. 1999 *The Simpler? Polyhedra* Nattygrafix
Taylor, P. 2009 *Flixton: Neolithic Lunar Observatory* Polystar Press
Taylor, P. 2009 *Seahenge: Sun Sand and Winter Solstice* Polystar Press
Taylor, P. 2010 *Lawford: A Timber Circle Overlooked* Polystar Press
Taylor, P. 2011 *Arminghall: Woodhenge of the East* Polystar Press
Thom, A. 1967 *Megalithic Sites in Britain* Oxford UP
Thom, A. 1971 *Megalithic Lunar Observatories* Oxford UP
Thom, A. & A.S. 1978 *Megalithic Remains in Britain and Brittany* Oxford UP

ACKNOWLEDGEMENTS

The author wishes to thank the many people who have, unwittingly or otherwise, contributed to this publication: David Nuttall for starting me off whilst he still worked for Suffolk Archaeology Unit; Stuart Boulter for taking me seriously enough to have my findings on Flixton checked; and various copyright holders for their kind permission to reproduce illustrations: Norfolk Archaeological Unit, Norfolk Historic Environment Service, Suffolk County Council, Essex County Council, Bedfordshire Archaeological Council, Cambridgeshire Archaeological Committee, Fenland Archaeological Trust, Cambridge University Press, Oxford University Press, East Anglian Archaeology, The Royal Archaeological Institute, The Ashmolean Museum

ALSO ABOUT THE EAST:

The Toll-houses of Suffolk Patrick Taylor 2009
Polystar Press ISBN 978 1 907154 00 3 iv+84pp £7.95

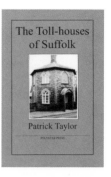

A comprehensive survey of the toll-houses of Suffolk,
dating mainly from the 18th and 19th Centuries.
Illustrated with an extensive gazetteer, and an appendix
covering buildings that might be mistaken for toll-houses.
"This useful study of an under-valued and threatened
building type is therefore to be welcomed"
Suffolk Historic Buildings Group

The Toll-houses of Norfolk Patrick Taylor 2009
Polystar Press ISBN 978 1 907154 02 7 iv+76pp £7.95

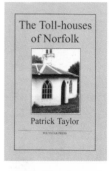

Research interrupted by the Norwich Library fire finally
resumed and brought to publication.
Essentially the same format as the Suffolk volume: history
of the turnpike roads, detailed gazetteer of the county etc.
"timely and important records of those that survive and
also those - sadly the majority - that have been lost"
Norfolk Industrial Archaeology Society

The Toll-houses of Essex Patrick Taylor 2010
Polystar Press ISBN 978 1 907154 04 1 iv+80pp £7.95

Following on from the Suffolk and Norfolk books, a
comprehensive survey of the toll-houses of Essex, dating
mainly from the 18th and 19th Centuries.
Illustrated with an extensive gazetteer, and an appendix
covering buildings that might be mistaken for toll-houses.
"... this is the first comprehensive account of Essex toll-
houses and it is a fascinating study. "
Essex Society for Archaeology and History

The Toll-houses of Cambridgeshire Patrick Taylor 2011
Polystar Press ISBN 978 1 907154 06 5 iv+80pp £7.95

And so to Cambridgeshire to complete the survey of toll-
houses in the eastern counties.
Essentially the same format as the other volumes: history
of the turnpike roads, detailed gazetteer of the county plus
an appendix on the impostors.
"Highly recommended"   Winner of Cambridgeshire
Association for Local History Book Award 2012